TECHNOLOGICAL PLANNING
ON THE CORPORATE LEVEL

TECHNOLOGICAL
PLANNING
ON THE CORPORATE LEVEL

Proceedings of a Conference Sponsored by
The Associates of the Harvard Business School

SEPTEMBER 8 and 9, 1961

EDITED BY JAMES R. BRIGHT

HARVARD UNIVERSITY
GRADUATE SCHOOL OF BUSINESS ADMINISTRATION
BOSTON • 1962

Library of Congress Catalog Card No. 62-11388

Foreword

THE growing influence of technological change on the business-man's problems and fortunes has increasingly concerned many of the Harvard Business School Faculty. Individual Faculty members have been introducing teaching materials in their own courses that recognize the influence of scientific progress, research and development activity, and new technological capability. I was fortunate in persuading Dean Stanley Teele, Associate Dean Russell Hassler, and my colleagues on the MBA Board that we should do a bit of "R & D" ourselves through an experimental attempt to teach a course directed at the problems unique to "technological innovation." Since 1960 our *Research Seminar in Technological Innovation* has been under way. Through it, I believe, we have obtained a modestly increasing degree of understanding and effectiveness; and a rapidly increasing confirmation in the essential vitality and soundness of the concept. Much of our course development, inspiration, and help has come from industry, through certain thoughtful managers, engineers, and scientists who are grappling with the business problems arising out of technological change and development.

When The Associates of the Harvard Business School offered the opportunity to assemble some experienced contributors around this topic, the timeliness and potential usefulness were too good to pass up. This program was planned to serve what seemed to be a neglected aspect of the area — top management's understanding of and role in technological planning.

The speakers were selected because each of them was known to be effective and had a special experience to offer on some facet of the topic. No pretense was made that any paper would be the definitive end-all, or that collectively the papers would provide comprehensive analysis of the problem. We deliberately distributed speakers' contributions throughout the spectrum of the topic

v

— from the broad viewpoint of corporate philosophy, down through specific tasks as far as evaluating research proposals and results. Each contribution was intended to offer one person's viewpoint and to provide the springboard for a discussion by an audience limited to 125 executives from member firms.

The results of the program were most gratifying. Our speakers' talks were useful, interesting, and often highly provocative. The whole tone was one of informality and useful exchange. In most cases the speakers simply "talked around" their manuscripts, so that these printed pages do not fully reflect their contributions. Discussion in several instances ran longer than the talks. I regret that we have been unable to capture and reconstruct the full coverage and flavor of challenge and contribution that were revealed in these discussions. The reader may be able to get some feeling for that atmosphere in the discussions following the papers by O'Brien, Ansoff, and Teller. Others were equally vigorous, but we were unable to pick up the exchanges as the speakers moved about the floor.

At the conclusion of this day-and-a-half program, we promised to provide participants with these printed proceedings. All papers appear here in the order of their presentation during the conference. Dr. Edward Teller gave the dinner speech on the evening of the first day, and a manuscript prepared from his recorded remarks follows the sixth paper in this volume. Excerpts of all discussions are given after the respective papers. In the interests of space we have omitted those visual aids that were used only to add variety to oral presentation.

Once more I wish to thank these speakers who gave this conference such vitality and enthusiasm.

JAMES R. BRIGHT
Professor of Business Administration

Soldiers Field
Boston, Massachusetts
October 1961

Table of Contents

Speech of Welcome

STANLEY F. TEELE

Dean, Graduate School of Business Administration
Harvard University

IT is my pleasure to welcome you to this conference on technological planning. There are two principal reasons why I am very happy indeed that we are having this conference. In the first place, it seems to me that the topic is both timely and appropriate. I have a very firm conviction that the principal fact affecting business and the business manager is the accelerating rate of change. Your presence here obviously shows your awareness of this with respect to technological matters, but as you look at many other aspects of life — at the growth of population and change in its composition, at the urbanization which is taking place all over the world, at the rise in economic and social expectations of the peoples of the world, at changes in agriculture which I think in this country at least are more important and more extreme even than any other kinds of changes — all of these, it seems to me, support the proposition that accelerating change is the most important single factor with which business managers need to be concerned in the present and future. It seems to me that there are a lot of consequences of this fact. I think that the premium on imagination, on flexibility, on the capacity to deal with questions that have never been asked before, will be very much more substantial than it has been in the past. I think that the capacity to deal with new knowledge effectively, new knowledge (both technical and nontechnical), which is piling up at a rate that is hard to exaggerate, is of the utmost consequence. It demands the capacity not only to acquire and use knowledge but also to discriminate carefully with respect to what does not need to be acquired and what should be avoided. Similarly, it seems to me that this creates the need for a kind of inner serenity on the part of the business manager that is greater than we have known before and that comes primarily from a full realization and full acceptance of the importance to society of the business manager's job. Without this, it seems to me, it is almost impossible to tolerate

1

the changes that we will face increasingly. Therefore, any opportunities to consider how you manage change, and I take it that is what planning essentially means, is of the utmost consequence.

I am also pleased that this is a conference for executives from among the members of The Associates of the Harvard Business School. This is a group of companies, as most of you know, which have associated themselves with the School financially and in other ways. The Associates, so far as their financial support of the School goes, are of the utmost importance to us. And this is one small way we have of saying "thank you" to those companies.

This conference has been planned by Professor James Bright and by Guinn Smith, who is the Director of The Associates. On behalf of the School I should like to thank them and I should like particularly to thank the participants who have given of their time and effort so generously. We are truly grateful.

I think a word or two about Professor Bright might be appropriate before I turn the meeting over to him. Professor Bright, as many of you know, has acquired literally a world-wide reputation in the area of materials handling and in the area of automation. More recently, and perhaps you are not so familiar with this, he has added to his areas of interest or at least expanded his emphasis on the whole area of technological innovation. He has carried on for the School research in this area, trying to determine what is being done, trying to throw light on a crucial question to us, which is: How can innovation be encouraged and improved? He has also been conducting a seminar here at the School in the area of technological innovation. It is therefore with very substantial pleasure and confidence that I turn this conference over to Professor James Bright.

PROGRAM INTRODUCTION

Technological Change as a Force in Business

JAMES R. BRIGHT

Professor of Business Administration
Graduate School of Business Administration
Harvard University

THIS program properly begins with my grandmother. About eight years ago, upon hearing a radio announcement of a missile shot of some then prodigious distance and speed, she remarked to me how things had changed since her youth. She told me of her trip through Yellowstone Park in a stagecoach, accompanied by an escort of cavalry; and she recalled that Custer's Last Stand took place barely 75 years ago. When she was a girl, the steam locomotive, the steamship, and the telegraph were the accepted technological devices in the social and business environment. Food was preserved to a substantial degree by home canning and drying procedures. Only nature's fibers were used in textiles. Kerosene and gas were the principal illuminants, with electric lighting still a curiosity. And around the home human and animal muscles were the principal sources of power.

Upon her essentially agrarian life, one development after another made impacts that changed her world. She saw the automobile and motor truck completely alter her concepts of neighbors, commodities, shopping facilities, and the scope of local businesses. She saw the airplane change from an amusing and even impossible idea into a curious reality, then into a daring, adventuresome thing, and finally into the accepted means of transportation. It annihilated her concepts of geography. She experienced the pleasure, convenience, and value of the telephone, she marveled at the advent of radio; but she could only shake her head in amazement at having living, talking pictures in her home. One of the great changes of her lifetime was the use of energy for home and farm use: Portable mechanical energy — the gasoline engine — was harnessed to hundreds of laborious tasks, giving them an entirely different time and cost structure. Electrical energy, which could be subdivided and controlled by a flick of the fingers, took the terrible drudgery out of household chores. As canning and bottling processes improved, she began to decrease time devoted to the preservation of food. When the first mechanical refrigerator stood in her kitchen around 1925, the whole business of food preservation lost much of its time requirement. And toward her last years frozen foods eliminated many food preparation duties. She also began to favor man-made fibers such as rayon and later nylon over natural fibers for some things. Truly her world had been remade and her way of living had been recast by a half a century of technological advancement. Consider, now, that each of these technological advances built new businesses; and many of these new businesses destroyed or radically altered their predecessor institutions.

As startling as these things have been, it seems that they are far from over. Indeed, I believe that the principal factor affecting the business world and our economic and social life today is the fact that these changes are accelerating in degree and, perhaps, in kind. Man's ability to control his physical environment seems to be growing rapidly. Can we identify the directions of these changes? I would define today's technical trends in six categories. I believe that we can see since, say, 1945-1950, new capacity with respect to the following:

1. Increased ability to master distance and time for the physical transport of men and goods. Moreover, we are on the threshold of new transportation capabilities in the mediums other than the surface of the earth and the atmosphere. These technological advances are just beginning to take us under the oceans and through outer space.

2. Increased ability to generate, store, transport, guide, and control energy. It is especially significant that this energy is of greater intensities — for both destructive and constructive purposes — and that it comes from sources and devices not previously used. In addition to handling larger quantities of energy, it is apparent that man now can handle far more minute quantities with increased precision.

3. A growing capacity to change the properties of materials and to create new materials is very much a part of today's tech-

nological frontiers. Dr. Lee DuBridge of California Institute of Technology has called this "molecular engineering." The ability to design materials with properties to order, and to modify characteristics so that materials serve special needs, is surely one of the most basic considerations that will alter the economic future for many, many firms, for geographic areas, and even for some countries.

4. The mechanization of physical processes. Of course, many direct labor tasks have been mechanized. Mechanization is spreading rapidly, however, and is already deeply entrenched in the field of packaging. It is just beginning a vigorous spread into assembly operations and into inspection and testing. The mechanization of movement — materials handling — is well underway, including the mechanization of work feeding. And the first attempts to automate warehousing operations are now in operation. It is noteworthy, too, that the movement of intelligence — communications — is rapidly being mechanized. This applies not only on a vast geographic scale, but within the factory and the home as witnessed by two-way radio, industrial television, and the tape recorder.

5. The mechanization of mental activities. Perhaps the most dramatic and powerful mechanization event of our generation is the computer. It offers tremendous extension of man's ability to acquire, store, manipulate, interpret, and to select or supply data and other information.

While not as dramatic, a rapid development of program control techniques has given new capabilities for manless operation of machinery and precision of a distinctly higher order than in the past. Tape-controlled machines and the punched-card programs as instruction devices enable the imposition of complex instructions on machinery. Feedback control — the ability to sense the variable in the environment and adjust to meet its requirements — is introducing new capabilities in the process industry and in many other fields.

6. Finally, we note that the ability to prolong the useful life of both animate and inanimate objects is growing. The reduction of the death rate among human beings is perhaps a fundamental factor affecting our society. In a less dramatic but quite significant way it is apparent that we have growing capability in freezing, drying, and preserving techniques for food; and of techniques

that reduce corrosions, insect damage, weathering, and other deleterious effects on materials and equipment.

While many of these technological developments are built upon previous technical advances and opportunities opened by new scientific knowledge, it is clear that there also are several major social influences affecting technological advances. The few items singled out below are by no means all the forces at work; nor do I know how to describe their relative importance. It simply seems to me that here are three social factors that today inspire, underwrite, or alter technological progress to a very great extent:

1. The severe growth in population. In the 1930's and for the few decades previously the United States lived with a population relatively stable at around 130 million. By 1960 this had increased to approximately 180 million and there are claims that by 1980 it will be upward of 240 million, rising to over 300 million by the year 2000 A.D. This will surely produce an impact on our natural resources that will alter the cost structure of many materials and thus produce a web of technological changes. Meanwhile, the rest of the world's population is exploding at a frightful rate with a net effect that the demand for food, raw materials, and finished goods will increase in such a way that traditional sources of supply will not be adequate, and costs surely will not stay in the same relative relationships. It is easy to anticipate an eventual competition for many raw materials as the world supply dwindles and local populations demand more for home consumption.

2. The rising standard of living in Europe, in Japan, and no doubt in many other countries, as well as in the United States. This will mean a growing per capita consumption of goods. Coupled with the population increase, pressure on natural resources will be even more severe. Consider this country's adoption of the automobile: First, it became an indispensable part of family life; then the need for a second car became an accepted idea in millions of families. From one radio (and now one television set) per family we have seen a spread of multiple units in each household. While many have strong doubts as to the desirability of this affluence, commercial and economic forces certainly encourage further movement in these directions, with the inevi-

table consequence that each member of society requires more materials and energy.

3. The growing role of the government in technological support. It is striking that since World War II the government has become the biggest single customer of business even in a peacetime economy. This customer demands products of a most incredible complexity, continually refined and more advanced. Usually performance considerations far outweigh cost considerations. These technological advances are peculiar in that they are subject to what at times seem to be (and sometimes are) capricious political decisions. As the government's role in our economy increases, it follows that political decisions become in many instances the most important factor determining whether a line of technological progress shall be pursued, dropped, or superseded by another technological effort.

Rather than attempt to establish the business consequences of these broad trends at this time, I propose to leave that for the end of our conference and at the moment I will simply ask this audience one question: Have I missed anything significant?

Q. You forgot, I think, one heading of equal importance. This is the tremendous increase in our ability to sense things. Take radar, for example, or the electron microscope. We have tremendously increased our ability to find out what's going on in areas beyond our physical senses and this capability is clearly increasing.

A. I had thought of this as coming under the acquisition of intelligence.

Q. No, the extension of our sensory abilities is a technological trend in itself.

A. I agree that it certainly should be stressed.

Q. I think your Point 4 is in direct contradiction to your statement about the automated factory.

A. These things are by no means universal or exclusive.

Q. Have you included in No. 6 our ability to control, to systemize, to subordinate?

A. Yes, it's probably in Item 6. Maybe I haven't expressed it as eloquently as I should to dramatize the significance of control. All of these trends imply new ability in control.

Q. Could you make Point 4 read backwards? Technological change can alter political decisions?

A. That's a good point. Technological change can alter the political affairs as we all well know. However, the focus of this conference is on technology.

Q. To what extent has the generation of capital been responsible for our ability to do these things today?

A. Here's a question that I must respond to very carefully so that I won't be misunderstood. Ability to extend these trends implies, first, getting the idea and developing the scientific background and theory. I'm not at all sure that this takes much capital. But the translation of a scientific idea into commercial reality — in other words, development — is something else. There I am sure that we need enormous amounts of capital. Take atomic energy, for example. Who could have developed it but the government? So I can't formulate a quantitative answer to your question, but I'm sure capital availability has been a major factor in many instances.

Q. Another social trend is that of the changing character of ownership — from extreme private to broad public ownership.

A. Yes, the character of ownership seems to be changing from private to public and quasi-public in this country in some industries. This has great implications for the support and resistance of innovations.

Q. I'm surprised that you didn't include what brought this conference into being — the general acceptance of change as a normal factor. We all know that the history of development for many years ran into resistance on the part of the public. I know that's true on the part of nylon and all that. There's quite a different climate now. The door is open for all available developments.

A. The climate of acceptance? Would you mark this occurrence by a date or an era?

Q. I'm not a scholar, but I remember back in my own life — 1928 — that was the last year of the Model T Ford.

A. All right.

Q. I think it goes back at least to the 1890's or so when the great economists created a definite feeling that civilization had changed, and now would accept a great deal of change, while before we would not.

Q. Do you feel that competitive pressures are sharper today than they were fifty years ago? I think we all believe this in industry. For example, in my new division (electronics), we've been in business for a few years. From a statistical basis, we don't have a single product yet of a profitable nature. This is not real obsolescence;

it is technical competition. It is innovation. It is urgent change. If we don't do anything about it, I'm going to be hungry in 1966.

A. Perhaps we should review our list of technical factors. It seems clear that the first significant consequence is that we have many new sources of competition. Where is the security in mastery of a given material? Where is the security in mastery of a certain source of energy? Or in counting on a geographic barrier for market protection? I think all these developments suggest great implications for competition.

Now let's move on to our first speaker.

BETTING ON NEW TECHNOLOGIES

RICHARD C. RAYMOND

RICHARD C. RAYMOND

Manager, Technical Military Planning Operation
Defense Systems Deparment
General Electric Company
Santa Barbara, California

Dr. Raymond's education was in the field of physics. He received his B.S. from Washington State University and his Ph.D. from the University of California. After work at M.I.T. Radiation Laboratory and the Harvard Radio Research Laboratory, he taught at Pennsylvania State University and worked with Haller, Raymond & Brown, Inc.; later he joined the RAND organization at Santa Monica. In 1956 he organized General Electric Company's unique Technical Military Planning Operation, which is devoted to the appraisal of developments having significant implications for the defense products of his company.

Betting on New Technologies

I'm going to talk around a business game. Scholars used to say that what they did not know they explained to each other. Nowadays, businessmen say, "What I do not know, I will explore in a game."

I will introduce later two of the research tools appropriate to success in this particular game. First I would like to describe my game in terms with which many of you are familiar.

In common with many of the other games, this one is only laid out and described; it is never played. It would be quite expensive, and anyway, its major virtues lie in the work of describing it and doing the research on strategy, and not in playing it.

My game is a horse race. It is not one which would be sanctioned under the laws of most of our states at the present time. Let's drive out to the track and see how it operates.

As we enter the parking lot, we note that the activities are already in progress. In fact, the track is open twenty-four hours a day, seven days a week. Racing never ceases. People are coming and going continuously. If we are extremely astute observers, we notice another thing right away. On the average, the people who are leaving are wealthier than those coming in. Instead of being a place where the players are relieved of money for the support of the track-owners and the state government, our track is one which produces wealth for the players and owners as well as the government. Many players lose and many win. The average effect is positive.

As we move from our parking place to the gates of the grandstand, we are accosted by touts. These are not the kinds of confidence men that one usually finds at a racetrack parking lot. They are engineers, scientists, inventors, and struggling small businessmen. There is also a sprinkling of investment counselors, security analysts, and business school professors. They are peddling everything from tips on sure winners to systems and studies of systems for picking winners.

The price of admission to the grandstand is nominal. We notice that in addition to the usual betting windows, bar, restaurant, and public restrooms, there is also a large hotel with rooms facing the track. It is well occupied by people who spend most of their time here. Entering near the top of the grandstand and taking our seats, we are impressed by a great state of confusion. A race seems to be in progress, for there are many horses on the track. Yet the track is a continuously changing steeple-chase affair. Crews of maintenance men are busy at all times installing and removing jumps and hazards and changing the route to be run. There is no well-defined starting gate. Horses in a variety of racing dress are entering at random intervals at various points around the track. Once on the track, their behavior is far from usual. Some run in the right direction for a while, then casually turn and run back. Some lie down and rest. Some die. Some leave the track through side gates. Many are eliminated by falls at the ever-changing hazards.

There are also many fouls committed. Horses crowd each other into the rail, kick each other, and carry out other interfering maneuvers with only casual and desultory attention from the track stewards. As we grow somewhat accustomed to this confusion, we notice also that betting on a horse never closes. There is a tote-board, but it is running far behind in its computations. It does not even carry listings for many of the horses which have entered the track most recently. We are continually importuned by agents representing particular stables or particular horses to place bets on their horses because most horses cannot stay on the track, particularly near the finish line, unless large and increasing amounts of money are bet on them.

Horses cross the finish line at random — some at a walk, others at full gallop. From those which cross, a very few are selected by the judges as winners. The owners and bettors are rewarded handsomely.

At first glance, it appears that the judges are crazy. There seems to be little relationship between the pay-off to a winner and its speed in running around the track or its appearance as it crosses the finish line.

We soon realize that if we are to exploit anything better than blind luck in betting at this track, we must pay attention to a great deal more than the nature and condition of the horses. We must also have due regard for the riders, for the changing difficulties of the race course, and for the choices and resources of the judges.

To put this into less fanciful terms, when we set out to bet on a new technology, we should know something about the technology on which we are betting, but we must also know the environment in which this technology is expected to perform, the person who is pushing it to perform and how the customers for this technology will decide how much to reward it. You are going to hear a great deal more from others in this session on the evaluation of the technologies themselves — or, in our current analogy, the horses. I am going to spend most of my time on the track and the judges. The choice of people to ride the horses is extremely important, but I'm not going to talk about it. It is too obvious.

The track and the judges cannot really be disassociated. They are both parts of the broad-scale environment in which a horse will either fail or succeed. I should like, however, to describe them separately in terms of a pair of research tools which we have developed over the last few years. The first of these tools is the broad-scale environmental study. It is an attempt to describe the condition of the track, not only now, but also in the future when we hope our horse will run and cross the finish line. The second tool, which can help us guess the decisions of the judges, we call a comparison of customer choices. It is a derivative of operations research and market research techniques. While looking at these tools separately, we will be ever-mindful of the fact that this separate consideration may introduce errors which must be eliminated when we try to combine our results to place intelligent bets.

The environmental factors study has been a part of market research and product planning for some time. I tend to be rather critical of the ones I have seen. They are seldom broad enough in scope and concept, and they too often cover ignorance by the simple process of extrapolation.

To be successful, a technology must serve a human want. This may be an existing want, or one which is created as a result of this or some other technology. In our broad-gauge environmental factors study, we must seek to establish the human wants which will exist in the time period when our technology can be effective. We must examine the competing technologies which can also serve these wants. In our comparison of customer choices, we must try to estimate how much our potential customers will be willing to pay in money and other resources for the satisfaction of these wants in comparison with all of their other wants.

I do not intend to get into the fundamental philosophic argument between the people who believe in determinism and those who believe in uncertainty. I will confess that I do not know enough to predict the future in any great detail. On the other hand, I will say that there are some aspects of the future that can be predicted with reasonable degrees of confidence. From these it is possible to draw some conclusions about the environment in which we hope to win our bet on a new technology. The geography and geology of the earth do change, but very slowly in relation to the other things about which we are talking. We can rely quite confidently on much of what we know about the earth sciences. Similarly, human physiology is in effect constant over ten or fifteen years. We can rely on many things about it. The so-called laws of physics have undergone very considerable revision since the beginning of this century. More can be expected. Nonetheless, many of the older fundamental relationships seem to have held quite firm. We should not bet heavily, for instance, on a perpetual motion machine or an information system that attempts to defy the laws of thermodynamics.

From the standpoint of the bettor on new technologies, one of the most significant changing elements of our times is the population explosion. While this factor might seem quite remote from a decision as to whether or not to put a particular item into production, it is nonetheless a fact that many of our technological opportunities and many of our business problems will flow directly from the interaction between expanding populations, expanding economies, limited real estate, developments in competing technologies, and our very limited understanding of the principles of social organization.

I should like to mention a few examples of technological prediction from the broad-scale environmental factors studies which General Electric has been sponsoring over the last few years.

We were able to predict several years ago that machines would begin to find their way into the field of education in large numbers in the current decade. This prediction resulted from an examination of the age distribution of the United States population, a basic understanding of information technology, and an economic understanding of the fact that the principal justification for increased pay to teachers as well as to any other class of people must lie in increased results. While the school-age population is due to continue its recent rapid increase for some time into the future, the working-age population will increase much less rapidly. This means that it will not be possible to fill the ranks of teachers at current or past pupil-teacher ratios without accepting poorly qualified personnel. A better alternative would be to increase the productivity of good teachers with educational machinery and thus meet the demand and justify higher pay to the more productive teachers.

Another reading which can be gained directly from the relationship between the exploding population and the finite size of the world is that it may well be essential to develop nonagricultural sources of food within the next forty years. Basic science tells us that farming, even by Japanese output standards, is very inefficient from a thermodynamic standpoint. There is lots of room for improvement, even if we use only solar energy in our new processes. The need for new food sources would be hard to see without looking at the problem on a global scale. In the United States we are currently spending vast amounts of money to produce food which is then placed in storage until it can be disposed of in a degraded form. This process will undoubtedly stop during our lifetimes, however. A very long-range business plan should contemplate a shortage of agricultural food, even in the United States, rather than an abundance. When we bet on a new technology, we often fail to take any account at all of the world outside our borders. More and more, we are finding this an unwise policy. Even if we are not involved in marketing overseas, we often face stiff competition from overseas manufacturers in this country. The whole process by which we devise and market our products and services is affected by the political stability of the world at large.

Out in Santa Barbara we spent most of last year with a small mixed crew of educated people looking at the problem of world political stability. We were particularly interested in the destabilizing influences of the large fraction of world population that lives in areas that are known in modern political parlance as the new and emerging states. We find, in general, that there will be a close race in many areas between population growth and economic growth even if we and the other industrially mature states pump in as much capital as these areas can possibly use to promote their expansion, and if the local governments in those areas are strong enough to use the capital properly and to stabilize a condition conducive to growth. The total amounts of capital which can be used properly are not significantly different from those which are now going into foreign aid and foreign investment, but economic and industrial development of these poor nations is far from the only problem. One thing that history has shown us time and time again is that economic and industrial development is accompanied inevitably by social and political change. Unless the economic and industrial development is accompanied by education and the growth of a culture which can properly include industry, there is continuous political instability. This instability finds its expression in external warfare almost as often as in internal revolution.

When we reflect that by 1975 twenty or thirty more nations may be able to arm themselves with nuclear weapons, we see that it is going to be difficult to tolerate this kind of instability. At the same time, the virus of extreme nationalism, which has more or less run its course in western Europe, has induced a high fever in the new states in Africa and South America. We see that there is very little occasion for a calm forecast of peace in our time.

The United States will very probably continue to assume an increased share of the commitment for stability of the boundary between the Communist World and the Free World. This commitment will become so large that it will be felt in every home and every office in the country. I suspect that the next fire call will be a good deal more noticeable (and hopefully a good deal more successful) than the Cuban affair. As I write this, Berlin seems to be high on the list of trouble spots. I cannot help the suspicion, however, that the Berlin issue is being raised to divert our attention from our defeat in Laos and from Communist moves into Southeast Asia, Africa, and Latin America.

Some of our businessmen who are now suffering the burden of Japanese competition should be interested in the growing power and threat of the Peoples' Republic of China. It is probable that the Chinese will be able to deploy their own nuclear weapons within the next few years. They may use these to frighten the people of Japan into the Chinese orbit and out of ours. If we should encourage such a move, we might be in the condition of the man who invited a tiger into his house to help him get rid of the mice. One of the recent events which seems to be working against Chinese ability to carry out this action is the failure of the central government to plan Chinese agriculture correctly. Our Government might have told them a lot about agricultural planning, although neither government seems to have made an outstanding success in the field. The history of China over the past few centuries would promote the conclusion that the central government will fall as the result of its agricultural failure and the food riots, some of which have already occurred. I submit that the present central government of China is different from the ones which have fallen. I do not know whether this one can survive, but I know that it may make a lot of trouble for us either way. During the last decade the people of mainland China have come under control of the first really effective central government since Genghis Khan. Through modern communications, secret police, hard work, Russian help, a fundamental invention in Communism, and a burning conviction of destiny, the government of Mao Tse Tung has established itself in command of the largest population on earth.

After flirting with family planning in the early fifties, this government decided that such a step was contrary to Marxism. It now faces a serious struggle for survival. The weather has combined with agricultural planning to leave far less than enough food to go around. If the central government does fall or is seriously weakened, we will get a little more time to think about our problem. If, on the other hand, it chooses external aggression as a way of uniting its people behind it, then our troubles will come sooner.

So long as the Chinese cannot threaten to use nuclear bombs, we can rely on the poor Chinese industrial mobilization base to keep them from fielding and maintaining a large modern army. With nuclear bombs, however, they can cover a series of small aggressions without a need for a large modern army. They can exploit the fact that China has much less to lose from an intercontinental war than either the United States or Russia. There is certainly no way of predicting anything with confidence here, but it would not surprise me to find in 1965 or 1970 that we are implicitly aligned with the Soviet Union against the Chinese. We may also have an expeditionary force in the southwest Pacific helping to defend Australia from the greater east-Asia co-prosperity sphere under Chinese management. If you have a business or trade relationship with Japan or if you are considering doing business with the Russians, it is interesting to think about the next ten years from these standpoints.

As a final item in the area of broad-scale environmental factors, I shall mention the doomsday machine and the general field of disarmament — or, more properly, arms control.

Technology is so prolific these days that we can talk with some assurance about weapons of almost any size for almost any purpose. We can operate under the seas, on the land, or in outer space. Since 1945 there have been fantastic increases in the zone of destruction that can be accomplished with a single weapon, and the detonation of such a weapon is directed by a single decision — right or wrong. True, these things are expensive, but the destruction is much cheaper per square mile than ever before. If, for example, we were to assemble most of the uranium available in the United States into a single bomb, it could produce a single explosion of perhaps 40 or 50 million megatons. Such a weapon would be far too small to create a supernova or even to break the earth in two, but it would be big enough to make its further habitability by the human race quite questionable. It would produce a truly gigantic earthquake. It would produce violent winds over a large area of the earth. It would produce about 400 times the amount of Strontium 90 needed to poison the whole earth against habitation.

Rational people would not build such a device today. They would certainly not use it if built. On the other hand, there is very little doubt in my mind that Adolph Hitler certainly wished that he had something like it during his last days in Berlin. A number of other possibilities in this area have come up. Paradoxical and incredible as they seem at the moment, they must at least enter our consciousness when we face the immediate question of disarmament. I prefer the term arms control because it can be defined in two packages. In one package are the measures which we must take as a nation to provide for executive control over the design, deployment, exercise, and use of our own armed forces. In the second package are international agreements, either formal or implicit, which are observed by collections of governments over the design, deployment, and exercise of their military forces. In this field, as in many others, it is obvious that we cannot enter an international agreement properly unless we have our own house in order. Further, it is quite possible to spend a lot of time sparring in the international arena on subjects which, though related to the general problem, are really trivial unless the general issues are attacked.

The historians of technology have characterized various ages in the past as stone, bronze, iron, steam, and so forth. I would venture to characterize the revolution which is sweeping us into the next age — if we survive to enjoy it — as the information revolution. I made a rough estimate a couple of years ago of the ability of the typical executive to deal with his daily flood of facts and figures. It turns out that, on a quantitative basis, you have time to receive and absorb somewhere between one-thousandth and one-hundredth of the information which is available to you that might significantly affect your decisions on the job.

We are developing an information technology which has become quite sophisticated in many respects, although it is antique in others. Your future in your business will probably depend more in the next decade on how you learn to marshal and apply the information relating to your business than on any other factor within your control. Frankly, I have little hope for many members of the current management generation. A few of them have not learned to use a telephone properly. Many have not learned to use a dictating machine. Practically none has learned to use a computer.

To revert to the race-track game, there are many items of information available to all of us with which we can improve the betting, but right now we are drowning in individual items and we have very little way of hooking them up and making a realistic picture suitable for the use of the bettors. There is no limit other than personal exhaustion to the effort we should make in defining the environmental picture and seeking its broad relationships with our business.

Now, while we're back at the track, I hope you will recall that we planned to look in some depth not only at the track itself — that is, the environment — but also at the judges. I said that we had a research tool useful in sizing up the judges, and that this tool hasn't yet acquired a good generic name; it derives from operations research and market research techniques. We call it tentatively a comparison of customer choices.

Generally, the objective of operations research is that of a cost-benefit analysis. In our horse-race game this is primarily a study of the horses. It often leaves out many of the environmental changes which may be expected as they go around the track. It usually ignores the jockeys, and it often ignores the judges more or less completely or, even worse, ascribes rational qualities to them. That is, it makes them think the way we do. While the cost-benefit analysis is a useful part of the whole process, it is so well understood that I am going to describe it only briefly. It involves selecting a human want to be fulfilled, doing preliminary engineering on a number of technologies which will meet this want with varying degrees of effectiveness, pricing the different systems out, and using mathematical models or other logical means to find the effectiveness of each system in comparison with its costs. If we then assume that the system which costs least for a given desired effect will always win, we assume that our judges have purely economic motives.

Economic man is a fictitious animal who was invented to try to put some kind of rationale into the choices which customers make as to how they wish to spend their resources. As a first rough cut, economic man is helpful, but we really need a description of emotional man — and preferably of *total* man — if we are to get closer to actual performance. I believe that a safe generalization can be made from experience that emotional man is in some senses a time-delayed economic man. What I mean here is that decisions which were reached on a rational, economic, and technical basis some time ago have only recently penetrated to the emotional level where real decision making occurs. Unfortunately, the situation is by no means this simple.

All descriptions and most thought processes take place through the use of words. As a semanticist would be quick to point out, words mean different things to different people. Unfortunately, simple misunderstandings or failures to define are often the key points in major decisions.

The tool which I would like to describe is not a substitute for human judgment. It is merely a tool which tends to bring out and focus those questions on which human judgment will be exercised by a customer. It has strong economic connotations because what it tries to do is to compute the dollar cost to a class of customers of each of a complete set of alternative choices. We have applied this tool with reasonable success to a large customer such as the United States Air Force. We have made some headway in devising the tool for application to other customers. We have not gone very far in applying it to a customer like an individual consumer of home products. Nonetheless, I should like to describe the tool in terms which might conceivably apply to any customer at all.

The first task in putting this tool together is to lay out as completely as possible a classification of the things for which the customer will spend his money. (Figure 1) In the military case we have been able to break these down under major weapons

EXAMPLE: U.S.A.F.

WEAPON SYSTEM	ACCOUNTING CATEGORIES				
SAC B-52 B-58 B-70 ATLAS TITAN MINUTEMAN ETC	\$ \$ \$ ↓ ETC	\$	\$	\$	\$
ADC • • •					
TAC • • •					
OTHER • • •					
TOTAL					

Figure 1

system classifications, and to assign the various categories in which military accounts are kept to these major systems by cost-allocation techniques.

The second task is to estimate, for a suitable period in the future, how much of each kind of product the customer will buy and what his inventory of these products will be. (Figure 2)

The third step (Figure 3) is to apply cost-analysis techniques to find out what it will cost the customer to purchase these products, to install them, and to operate and maintain them on a yearly basis. If our year-by-year estimate of his purchases and his inventories are good and if our costing procedure is correct, we should come out with the total of his budget for each year. If our estimate of his purchases and inventories is too large, as it usually is in market research, the costing will show us that he plans to exceed his budget. We will then be forced to use any other information we can get — and judgment as a backstop for lack of information — to decide which of his wants the customer will scale down in order to stay within his budget.

U.S.A.F.

WEAPON SYSTEM	FORCE STRUCTURE					
	1961	1962	1963	1964	1965	1966
SAC B-52 B-58 B-70 ATLAS TITAN MINUTEMAN ETC						
ADC • • •						
TAC • • •						
OTHER • • •						

Figure 2

In case we wish to bring a new product to the customer's attention during this period, we may also make some guesses based on this comparison of the changes he might make in his purchase and inventory plans if he is to buy our new product. I said earlier that the judges in our horse race are apparently crazy. There are some things we can learn about them, however. We can reach reasonably good approximations of the amounts of prize money they have available for offer. We can also study their past history in awarding prizes to different kinds of horses. Further, by more intimate personal knowledge of the individuals involved, we may often make some shrewd guesses as to the kinds of horses they will prefer in the future.

The tool of comparing the effects of these choices which I am offering does not in itself tell us what judgment decisions the

U.S.A.F. CAMP*

(*COST OF ALTERNATIVE MILITARY PROGRAMS)

WEAPON SYSTEM	FORCE STRUCTURE						R & D $						INVESTMENT $						OPERATING $						TOTAL $					
	61	62	63	64	65	66	61	62	63	64	65	66	61	62	63	64	65	66	61	62	63	64	65	66	61	62	63	64	65	66
SAC																														
B-52							$	$	$	$	$	$	→ETC																	
B-58							$	$	$																					
B-70							$	$																						
ATLAS							$																							
TITAN							↓																							
MINUTEMAN																														
ETC							ETC																							
ADC • • •																														
TAC • • •																														
OTHER • • •																														
TOTAL																														

Figure 3

customers — the judges — are going to make. Figure 4 merely illustrates the inevitable repercussions of changes in customer habits when he operates under a total budget which is limited. In this sense it gives us an opportunity to guess that if the customer buys a new product to satisfy a particular want, he will probably reduce his purchases and inventory of an older product designed to satisfy the same want. This is a simple case of competition.

There are many ways of classifying a customer's wants, and differing competitive relationships show up depending on how they are classified. If we take the simple subject of communication, for example, I might have stayed in my comfortable surroundings in Santa Barbara and addressed this meeting by telephone, or I might have put this address on film in advance and mailed it to you. As a matter of fact, I did not do either of these,

U.S.A.F. CAMP

WEAPON SYSTEM	FORCE STRUCTURE 61 62 63 64 65 66	R & D $ 61 62 63 64 65 66	INVESTMENT $ 61 62 63 64 65 66	OPERATING $ 61 62 63 64 65 66	TOTAL $ 61 62 63 64 65 66
SAC B-52 B-58 B-70 ATLAS TITAN MINUTEMAN ETC					
ADC MORE OF THIS MEANS LESS OF THIS	UP DOWN	UP DOWN	UP DOWN	UP DOWN	UP DOWN
TAC					
OTHER MAY MEAN MORE OR LESS OF THIS	? ?	? ?	? ?	? ?	? ?
TOTAL					ESSENTIALLY FIXED

Figure 4

but I came across the country by air to speak to you in person. If a more satisfactory technology of communication develops, I might elect to stay home and use it. When my wants are cut along this dimension, the airline industry is in competition with the telephone industry and the motion picture industry, and I suspect that my choices are influenced as much by habit and emotion as by rational analysis. In the military market at the present time, there is strong competition between the airplane makers and the missile makers to fulfill various kinds of wants for bombardment equipment. In the recreation area, manufacturers of television sets have long known that they were in competition with motion picture exhibitors, but I wonder how many of them have realized that they are also in competition for both consumer funds and consumer time, with manufacturers of pleasure boats or home workshop equipment? We have not succeeded in putting a time measure into this tool as yet, but I suspect that in some cases it is as important as a money measure.

I am not going to try to refine this tool to a point where any of you can take it home and use it. I do suggest, however, that a few hours on your part in trying to define and classify those human wants which you can serve, and in seeing what your competition really is, will contribute greatly to your understanding of the risks involved in a bet on a new technology.

The object of this whole exercise can be set according to the desires of the individual doing the betting. If he prefers to gain modest rewards from low-risk bets, he can select those items which appear to be sure things. If, on the other hand, he prefers to strive for high rewards from high-risk bets, he can make some estimate and base his selection on those. The traditional methods of operations research will help him to evaluate the horse and to estimate the size of the bet and the cost of the prize to the consumer. The broad-scale environmental factors study will help him to foresee the condition of the track — the future human wants which might not appear obvious on the basis of more limited investigation. The need for a good rider — a dynamic leader — if a new project is to succeed has been understood for a long time. The classification of customer wants and the summing up of how the customer may satisfy all his wants not only will help in estimating the risks and rewards of betting on a new technology, but will point out those products currently being made which are most vulnerable to competition from new ones.

As a final note, I should add that just as the racing game goes on twenty-four hours a day, seven days a week, this kind of objective analysis and evaluation of bets on new technologies is one which never stops. New technologies are superseded by newer ones. All of them compete in a variety of ways for customer attention. The customer decision process sometimes seems inscrutable. Life might be much simpler if the whole procedure were rational, but it would probably be much less fun.

Q. We are impressed at your point of the lead time between the response of economic man and emotional man. I think it would be appropriate to incorporate a few remarks about the lead time in Air Force-Military awareness relative to corporate activities. Why did you say that the response of economic and social man increased our limited technical budgets?

A. Remember that the launching of Sputnik served as a sharp excitation to the American public. If you compare *Life* magazine the week before Sputnik with *Life* magazine the week after Sputnik, they appear to come from different planets. Yet the first release of the overtime restriction on our missile work after Sputnik was sixty days! This is the "shock response time" of the U.S. administrative machinery! Within about twelve months after Sputnik the ripple had died out. You could write a transfer function for the United States government with a minimum delay of two months and an exponential of about six months' duration, something like this. . . .

Q. You propose that a business firm should be looking at broad-scale environmental factors such as Red China. Well, taking this broad political, social, historical look at China, what happened to the study you made? What did you do with it? What went to management? Did it carry recommendations? In what form?

A. One of the problems to which I've devoted a great deal of attention in my five years in TEMPO has been the problem of communicating with management. I cannot say that I have solved it. However, we do try to categorize our outputs and to prepare them in forms palatable for the level of management at which we are trying to shoot. To our top management is a one-page letter or a fifteen-minute briefing, or a phone call. To our upper middle management it is an executive summary kind of report, sometimes a personal call with a two-hour discussion. To our lower middle management it is a fairly lengthy report because there are so many of those people that we do not have the time to give them individual attention. We have roughly 2,000 customers in this latter category, and it would just be impossible to deal with them individually. We also distribute our unclassified work to university libraries in several places around the country and make it available to government agencies, and especially to the Armed Forces War Colleges.

Q. Do you take it upon yourselves to recommend management action, or do you only say, "This is what we think is happening?"

A. No, we do not normally recommend action. We may present alternatives and may present the results of pursuit of alternative strategies. We leave it up to the business decision maker to make the business decision, but we try to instruct him as well as possible.

Q. The last few charts you put up assume special significance because, with the fiscal year 1963, the Department of Defense budget will use practically this format, which Rand used for the first time. It's a fairly radical change in budgeting.

A. I have a prediction on that. The Air Force will be able to do it very easily because Rand has been doing it for them for a long time. The Navy may barely squeak through. We're helping them. The Army is going to have a great deal of trouble complying, because they haven't done anything in this way.

CRITICAL DECISION POINTS
IN TECHNOLOGICAL INNOVATION

DAVID B. SMITH

DAVID B. SMITH

Vice President of Technical Affairs
Philco Corporation
Philadelphia, Pennsylvania

Mr. Smith is a graduate of Massachusetts Institute of Technology. For many years he has been Vice President of Research for Philco. During the last three years his title has been Vice President of Technical Affairs. During this time he has concentrated on the task of evolving new products from and around new technology. Mr. Smith has participated in many conferences and programs, and has authored many papers dealing with the planning and management of research and development activities.

Critical Decision Points
in Technological Innovation

In these days, most companies are concerned as much with growth as they are with current profit . . . although the former is difficult without the latter. There seems to be a certain glamour associated with growth by technological innovation, although this is but one of several ways a company can grow. As a consequence, considerable attention is now being given to the management problems associated with technological innovation and some common management practices are beginning to emerge, at least in the growth-type industries of the "applied science" type — such as the electronics group, the petrochemicals, aircraft, and missiles group, etc.

Definition of Technological Innovation

I would like to define technological innovation as the process of developing new products to satisfy wants which have not heretofore been satisfied — and often not even recognized prior to the identification of the new product. In fact, usually it is the knowledge of the existence of the product that creates the need for it. This is in contradistinction to normal product improvement, even of major proportions. The automobile people, for example, could make a major change in the technical design of their automobiles, such as changing from a piston-type to a turbine engine, but that would not significantly change the total number of cars sold over a reasonable period of time, since the demand for automobiles is pretty well fixed by the size of the population. By contrast, the introduction of the new electronic component transistors cut into the vacuum tube business somewhat by displacing them in hearing aids, portable radios, and some military gear. But the great majority of transistors find their place in large computers and other electronic assemblies where the vacuum tube could not do the job. To a very large extent, transistors have made possible larger electronic systems not otherwise feasible, and this in turn has led to the development of a whole host of new devices, both of the end-product and component type.

A key characteristic, then, of successful technical innovation is that it provides a new product which creates its own market and in general branches off and induces a whole series of new commercial products. In effect, it is the spark which ignites a whole chain of events. Historically, all our great industries began in this manner.

People Problems

Now, the science of management is primarily the business of getting things done through people. People, in general, are creatures of habit and tend to resist change. To a considerable extent, present corporate structures are designed to take advantage of this human frailty, which tends further to enforce it. Yet, people do grow and mature, just as new products do. Their skills and abilities can be broadened with proper guidance. Technical innovation, by definition, requires people to change their habits, often their jobs, and certainly their way of thinking. So, an important management task is to arrange things so that the natural human resistance to change does not defeat the objective of innovation. Rather, management should couple the natural growth of its people with the development of its product. Creating the proper human environment and seeing to it that the proper people are selected and motivated to make the many decisions required in the course of the innovation process is the major management task.

There are at least three critical turning points in this management task which I wish to discuss today — both in terms of the human, as well as the technical, situation. The first is the inchoation problem — how do you initiate the growth process; the second is the transitional problem of moving from the scientific to the commercial phase; and the third is the problem of approaching maturity. Each of these phases has its identifying technical characteristics and each requires a different kind of human skill and aptitude. Each stage must be successfully mastered for the company to be successful.

INCHOATION

Strategic Use of Research

Let us consider first that group of decisions which management must make to initiate the innovation process. In a previous paper [1] I have discussed the strategic use of the research function for this purpose. Briefly, in a modern decentralized company, the objective of decentralization is to make it possible for a small group of people to concentrate their full time and attention upon a particular product area. This group is conventionally provided with all the elements necessary successfully to exploit this product field. That is, the group will include engineering, product development, production, marketing, etc. Within the corporation, it will constitute a profit center and will be expected to contribute current profits, as well as to protect its future by doing such advanced development as may be necessary to maintain its future profit position.

Limitations of Line Division

In such a situation, however, it will be observed that the chances of a major technical innovation taking place are small. All the individual incentives, all the policy decisions of such a group, should be predicated upon a relatively short-range time cycle and upon relatively sure technical bets. In these circumstances, it is unlikely that any major technological breakthrough will occur. In fact, a group under such policy directives could properly be criticized for undertaking scientific work of the character likely to lead to a major technical breakthrough, since such effort would not be in keeping with the basic company objectives which led to forming that profit center in the first place; i.e., the objective of having that small group of people concentrate upon a particular product area, specifically entrusted to them and to no other in the company, to exploit and develop for the benefit of the company as a whole.

It is for this reason that most companies find it desirable to have a separate research group — completely divorced from cur-

[1] "The Strategic Use of Research," AMA Report #30, *Ends and Means of Modern Management,* p. 48.

rent problems and normally charged with the objective of undertaking speculative research in the hope that it will lead to the technical breakthroughs that form the basis for growth by innovation. It is not logical to consider such a group a profit center, since they are rather remote from the actual pay-off. Indeed, it is necessary to insulate such a group from concern with current problems or immediate return on their effort if they are successfully to accomplish their objective of innovation. This is the principal reason for separating the research group from the operating divisions of the company.

An example of this is the development of color television. At the turn of the fifties, publicity concerning the need for color TV was rampant. I am sure many managements impressed upon their technical people the extraordinary importance of a technological breakthrough in this area. Yet, there were only three significant major developments — the RCA shadowmask receiver, the Philco "Apple" receiver, and the Lawrence tube. Both RCA and ourselves had research groups completely independent of the operating line divisions to work on the problem. In each case, we were able to do so without regard to the current technical problems of the line divisions — and there were many such problems at that time. The Lawrence tube was, of course, the product of an independent research group headed by Dr. Lawrence. The hundreds of engineers and scientists in the dozen or so big development laboratories of the many companies then engaged in the monochrome TV business were, I suspect, too preoccupied with their current problems and with the budget limitations inherent in a current profit center. In any case, that large group of knowledgeable people did not contribute any major technical advance in this area.

Likewise, management must be careful not to allocate the exploratory research funds too closely with the existing business. While such "seed corn" money will not be very large by comparison with the total expenditures necessary to get a major new business started, it will often seem large by comparison with the budget established for product development in a narrowly defined and mature product field. Yet, to grow by technical innovation requires boldness and a willingness to take chances. The mature product fields that are the company's current bread and butter businesses are the least likely field in which to find new product opportunities. They, in their maturity, must provide the funds for other ventures which will eventually replace them.

Summary of Inchoation Decisions

I suggest, then, that if a company wishes successfully to grow by technical innovation, the first major policy decision it must make to implement this decision is to establish somewhere within the company a group of capable technical people whose job it is to make the technical advances from which new products will come. It is essential that within the company there is a clear understanding that this group is not a profit center in the usual sense. The financial return from their expenditures will come later, from other groups. The measure of the success of this group is not in terms of dollars and cents, but in technical achievement. It must be protected from the distraction of current problems. Managment must have patience and not expect immediate results. Management must also be prepared to take some long-shot gambles and to swallow a number of failures and near misses for every successful innovation.

In my opinion, in a decentralized company the best way to obtain this environment and this function is to have a central research laboratory, separate from the line divisions, and operating under policies and budgets established by the corporate management. There must, of course, be coordination and liaison between such research division and the several line divisions; but the corporate management must be prepared zealously to protect the independence of the research group and to establish policies for it which will clearly indicate its basic objective — of providing the technical knowledge from which new products will later come.

Selection of Fields of Effort

If management has resolutely decided to create the necessary conditions outlined above to provide fertile ground for innovation, its next and immediate problem is to select the more specific objectives for this group. In what scientific fields is it to search? This is a difficult and critical decision area . . . first, because there is little information on which to base a decision and, second, because both scientific and management knowledge is necessary and there are sometimes difficult communication problems in such situations.

Let us first consider the problem from the point of view of the scientific group. The kind of scientist who generally does the best job of developing technical material suitable for innovation is likely to be motivated more by his thirst for knowledge than by his interest in a specific product. This is not to say that he is not interested in the commercial aspect of his work. He probably is. But, nevertheless, the thing that provides the strong inner drive that makes him stay up nights working is his desire to know more about a particular subject — and his personal satisfaction comes from acquiring this knowledge rather than making a new product. While he will know a great deal about his particular field of science, he cannot afford to become too involved in the arduous process of commercialization, since the one thing he must have is enthusiasm and the conviction that nothing is really impossible. He cannot afford the caution expected and required of a development engineer. The key point here, I believe, is that this type of person does not have a specific object or thing as his goal, but rather the conviction that, if he works in a particular field, he will make important discoveries — the nature of which cannot be foretold.

Management, on the other hand, even though accustomed to dealing with uncertainties, normally thinks in terms of products, production facilities, marketing and distribution problems, and the capital required to accomplish the commercial purpose. Occasionally there are clear-cut human needs which are easily recognized, if difficult of solution. We need, for example, a cure for cancer. We need a way for a human to communicate directly with a machine without the elaborate and time-consuming intermediate steps now required. But who could have predicted with assurance that the transistor would come from the study of solid-state physics, or that atomic energy would come from the study of nuclear physics — before the fact?

With respect to the commercial organization, it is the job of the corporate management to establish the broad objectives of the company. It should, at least with its existing business, be able to identify the general product areas, the quality of the product, the kind of market it seeks to exploit, its competitive posture, and so forth.

One should here be satisfied with fairly general statements. In our own case, for example, we consider ourselves primarily an electronic company, or "applied science" company. Because we support a substantial research and development effort, we have limited our field in electronics to those products having a high technical content. The reason for this is that we could not normally expect to be competitive with another company which did not have our R & D overhead, but such company could not compete technically with us. Therefore, we tend to stay in areas where our technical abilities are important enough commercially to carry their share of the load. It should be possible to make a number of generalizations of this sort which will reasonably well define the broad areas of immediate interest.

If, then, these are known and understood by the research group, they should be able to identify the technical areas in which they should be engaged in order to give tactical support to the operating divisions and wherein there is the hope of making significant advances which may form the basis for a major innovation within the existing framework of the company.

A more difficult question arises when the research efforts begin to lead outside the current commercial areas of the company. And this is quite likely to happen. The objective of management for this group, as I have outlined previously, is to obtain a broad-gauge, rather free-wheeling group of scientists. This is what it takes to develop the technical material which is the basis for innovation. This group is not restricted to specific product programs. In consequence, their interests will tend to range rather broadly over their particular fields and especially in the interdisciplinary areas which, at the moment, seem to be the most fertile. Likewise, the technical needs of a growth industry tend to change quite rapidly and develop new business opportunities, which must be explored — not only from a technical point of view — but also from a management one.

For example, in the mid-fifties the rather explosive developments in solid state physics were opening up many new possibilities in such items as infrared technology, radically new ways to produce various electronic components, thermoelectric devices, fuel cells, energy converters, and the like. Understandably, many of these were in areas in which our company had not heretofore been engaged.

From a managemet point of view, this created a quite complex problem of which fields should be explored and which not. At this stage of the program there was no clear technical understanding of where some of these developments might lead, but the one thing that was clear was that we would have to make significant changes in our marketing and production philosophy to take advantage of these possible developments.

One way to do this is to ask the question of your technical people: suppose you are completely successful in attaining your objective — where, then, do we stand? The answer may well be quite surprising — perhaps to you. In our case, we tried in this manner to obtain a vision of where the technology might go. In some cases, there were several possible paths which it might follow. We then considered in rather general terms how the company might take advantage of these possibilities, if they occurred, and how other companies similarly situated might respond. We also considered the relative advantage to us of these possibilities against other better understood and less risky programs, since there are always limitations as to how much one can attempt.

In this instance, one course of technology could lead to possible products useful to heavy industry. This would require us to compete in a field where we had no standing — no experience — no marketing — no production knowhow. This was not a very promising outlook. In another instance, the path seemed to be quite in line with our general business area, but would require substantial changes in our manufacturing skills. This we decided to pursue with vigor. In a third instance, it seemed possible that the eventual products would be related to our business, but we would have to develop new marketing skills and new production facilities. In this case, we decided that this would be worth pursuing — provided we could succeed in attaining technical breakthroughs which would give us a commanding technical position, but would probably not be worthwhile unless we could. We went ahead on this basis.

Such commitments for research programs do commit the company to a future course of action, with all that this implies as to management requirements, capital requirements, and so forth. As such, they should have the full support of the senior management of the company. Yet, in general, only the technical people have the requisite understanding of the science upon which to base such decisions. What is needed here is the comprehension of the strengths and weaknesses of the company as a whole. In a company that proposes to grow by technical innovation, there must be some key person or persons in the senior management who have such knowledge and can make such decisions.

THE TRANSITIONAL PHASE

A second major group of critical decision points arise when the research group has developed a body of new technical material from which new product possibilities are apparent. Let us consider two key questions which then arise:

(1) Is it possible to split out a product program and why should one do so?

(2) Should such a product program be entrusted to an existing division or should a new division be organized for this purpose?

The Nature of Research Results

A good research program should produce enough technical knowledge so that one can visualize a number of commercial uses of the information. The individuals who have produced this knowledge, however, have not been product-oriented in their thinking, nor have they likely had too much contact with the market place, nor with the whims and vagaries of possible customers. They could not have accomplished their mission if they had. So they are not well qualified to do a product development job. They can provide enough information, however, so that proper people in line divisions, with this knowledge and skill, can do this kind of planning. For example, several years ago we had completed a significant amount of research on thermoelectric materials. It was then necessary to make the first decision outlined above.

Here, the exploratory research had been well done and it was possible for the research group to give us:

(1) Quite complete information as to what could or could not be done with such devices;

(2) Where they would likely find uses in our company and the conditions necessary successfully to use them;

(3) What would be involved in the manufacturing operations; and

(4) What the future might promise in this area.

With this information, we were then in a position to ask the appropriate product development, market research, and manufacturing units in the line divisions concerned to make studies, based upon this information, of the impact of this technology upon the company. These studies showed that, even though this was a most promising new development, it was not one which our company — under the then existing circumstances — should go after from a manufacturing point of view. It also identified several specific research and engineering programs which we did establish.

The New Considerations

Now, let us consider the next step in a successful research program from which you wish to split out a commercial development program. Your research people are flushed with success and anxious to move forward. At what stage of the program should it be transferred to the line division? How do you do so without losing momentum?

The evolution of a basically new product requires many different skills and the efforts of many different kinds of people. The art of management is to assign these several tasks to the people best qualified to handle them at the right time and in such way as to promote the harmonious cooperation between the various participants.

As we have discussed, the technology is most likely to begin with scientists, not market-oriented and not distracted by current problems. As the technology begins to crystallize, however, then the importance of marketing considerations becomes paramount. At this stage of the development, it is necessary either to transfer the project to a commercially oriented group or, alternatively, to change the motivation of the technical people on the project by transferring them to a different environment. The technical objective now is no longer just to seek knowledge, but rather to identify a market opportunity and provide the product to suit it.

The Task for Management

It seems to me that at this stage three things are required of management: first, considerable vision to grasp the full implications of the raw material that research has provided; second, considerable commercial astuteness to be sure that the right questions are asked; and third, considerable knowledge of human nature to be sure that the new group who will now be entrusted with the program properly understand it and are properly organized to accomplish their mission.

It is an excellent idea to begin the development of a long-range plan in some detail at this point. This is the best way I know to identify the problems to which answers are required and to begin to identify the financial aspects of the program. It will clarify for all concerned the reasons for bringing in the new group of people and will help them identify the opportunity available to them. Of course, it is not likely at this time that a detailed and precise plan can be evolved. But what can be done is to develop the skeleton or outline of the new business venture; the flesh will come later — as the business develops.

Vision on the part of senior management is essential to enable it to grasp the implications and to fire the enthusiasm of others. One will never know the opportunities that have been lost because of management failure at this critical time.

Commercial astuteness is necessary. There are many conditions necessary to the success of a new product. This is why new ventures have such a high mortality rate. Usually these are not technical in nature and, at this point the people heretofore doing the actual work have been trained not to think about such problems. But now they must be identified and thought through. It is the job of senior management to see that such problems are identified and plans made accordingly. In my opinion, this can best be done by the long-range planning process. This exercise will identify the several kinds of experts necessary, but management cannot shirk the responsibility to provide the drive and initiative to determine that the problems are found and courses of action developed. It is not useful just to sweep the problems under the rug.

Finally, there is the critical decision as to whom to entrust this new opportunity. In the technical area, it is often the case that some of the research people who started the process will want to continue with it as it moves toward commercial reality. If they also wish to adopt the point of view required of a line division member, this is a good solution. Others in the research group will wish to continue with the research phase and will have little interest in the commercial part.

In the case of my company, many of our new businesses are now managed by research alumni who moved with the commercial program as it was split off from the research program and transferred out of the Research Division. Failing that, there must be an intermingling of research and development engineers while the information transfer takes place. But the best way to transfer information is to transfer people who have it. Normally, the hiring program of the research group will bring in some individuals who are really better suited to engineering. A proper and sound way to use such people is to assign them to programs which are approaching the point where a product is likely and expect them to develop with the product program and stay with it as it is transferred to a line division.

It is necessary to make the decision as to whether this new program is to be entrusted to an existing division or subgroup, or whether a new group is to be created to handle it. The key factors in such a decision will depend upon the company philosophy with respect to decentralization, etc. Usually, one seeks here to establish the boundaries or territory of a division or subdivision so that it encompasses a natural homogeneous market, product, or production area. The objective is to permit the group to become expert and highly competitive by narrowing the field which it must know and understand. It is desirable, therefore, not to have such singleness of purpose defeat the objectives for the new product, and if there is any real question of this with respect to product, marketing, or production philosophy, then it is better to plan for a new division or subdivision.

Just as the new product evolves, so the people who have been responsible for it will have matured. If this has been anticipated, then as the business needs of the program change, some of the people associated with the program will also have developed and will be able to grow with it and to accept the new responsibilities and different point of view required in the decision-making process. The ideal situation is one where enough such people can be kept in the program to maintain the drive and enthusiasm for it which brought it about in the first place.

Beside the usual criteria for defining the division boundaries, there is one other factor which I consider quite important. This is the question of the position that the proposed new product will occupy in the hierarchy of existing products. It is not desirable, even among the products of an established division, to have too large a spread between the volume and profit possibilities of the largest and smallest. Otherwise, the smallest will suffer from lack of attention and country cousin treatment. This is even more true of a fledgling new product, whose volume and profit potential are yet to be established and which will, for some time, be a drain upon the company's resources. It is, of course, desirable to get the new product going and on a profitable basis as soon as possible. On the other hand, it can be starved and will need financial support in the early stages. Not infrequently, this can best be done through the formation of a separate group or division so that the peculiar financial growth problems of this product are clearly separated from the different financial problems of the more mature products.

THE GROWTH STAGE

If one has a sound technical base, and if sound decisions have been made to provide a balanced, well-motivated group of people for the new product field, and if it has been well fitted into the company structure, it will — in all probability — enter into an explosive growth stage. The original product will likely have differentiated into a number of related products. There will, of course, be many conventional questions to be decided with respect to this thriving new business and these I do not intend to discuss. There are several major decision areas, however, which are peculiar to this growth stage and which constitute the third critical decision point for management in this process of technical innovation.

In our competitive environment, a business succeeds because on balance it has an edge on its competitors. New businesses created by technical innovation still have to exist in this environment and in all probability will have competitors. The basic problem now is to maintain this competitive edge in a rapidly changing situation.

The chances are that the business got started because of a strong technical situation. In the early days of transistors, for example, the race went to the one who could provide technical leadership. This is almost always true of growth industries. But technical leadership is an ephemeral thing. After a big forward surge in a new technical field, the scientific knowledge begins to spread, many more people are attracted to the field, and further major advances are harder to come by. Our national business philosophy is designed to bring about just this result. We encourage our scientists to publish technical papers, our military support of R & D programs disseminates considerable information, and our purchasing agents like second sources of supply. Now, it is not easy to recognize that the success formula of last year may not work next year, even though it is still working well this year. Nevertheless, this is the critical decision to make at this stage.

In the infancy of this new division, the premium was on technology and the natural leaders were technically trained people. Technology was the key to success. But now it is essential to develop other competitive advantages and skills in other areas. As the technology matures, it will be found that the needs of the customer will begin to dictate the design of the product. The emphasis now is not on what is technically possible, but rather on what is the best competitive solution to the customer's needs and wants. The number of products will increase to accommodate these specific needs. Effective marketing philosophies, efficient production and distribution become more important. In short, the business, as it matures, gets back to normal.

The problem for management is to foresee that this will happen and to guide the new division in such a way that it not only can cope with the evolution, but also take advantage of it. Again, the problem is to see that either the people evolve with the program or other people with the requisite skills are brought in and integrated with the group. Decision-making authority must be shifted within the several functional groups in accordance with these new conditions.

Conclusion

To summarize, the process of growth by innovation proceeds by stages which can be identified. Certainly there are at least three major ones. Each of these stages requires the special skills and talents of different kinds of people. These individuals all contribute their part in the over-all program, but each has different objectives and is motivated in different ways. The skill of management is to understand these different needs and objectives of these several groups, to establish the right objectives at the right time, and to have the sense of timing and understanding to effect the transition in an orderly manner from one group to the next as the development proceeds.

As the new technology evolves and new commercial products come into being, so also the organization that is responsible for this will evolve and mature. This organization is really just a group of people bound together by a common but changing objective. The most important task for management is to see to their development. This is really the essence of growth by innovation.

Q. You can't always legislate that all the good new ideas are going to come out of an organization formally set up for this purpose. How do you handle an idea if it arises from the operating side of one of your divisions?

A. This is a very good point. Our company has always tried to encourage new ideas wherever they may arise. Our experience has been that our research group, which constitutes perhaps 10% of our technical people, will provide something of the order of 70% to 80% of the new ideas. But there is this other 20%. Generally, what we do is to persuade the fellow, if it's really a good idea, to come over into the research group and to work on his idea at that point. But you've got to get it out from under the environment of the operating group. In other words, our real objective is to get the fellow with a good idea into an environment where he can, in fact, explore it. Usually, at this early stage, that environment is found in our research group.

Q. Wouldn't there be a problem of accepting him into the research group. Wouldn't there be jealousy or conflict of a sort toward a "foreigner" coming in with an idea?

A. No, we've not encountered that kind of trouble. I think technical people generally respect a fellow who has a good idea, no matter what his origin.

Q. Who decides what is a good idea?

A. There is a considerable amount of selling involved here. First of all, you have within a research group, just as you do in a line division, a group function to evaluate ideas and to crystallize them. Ultimately somebody must make the decision. In our company, if you want to think in terms of the final authority and if we're talking now about an existing business, it is usually the line division manager who has the final say. If it is a new area that we're going to get into, then this decision is made at corporate management level.

Sometimes these decisions just get made, and then it's "you do it!" In my judgment, this is wrong. What you really have to do is to sell these new ideas to the fellow who finally makes the decision. Don't do so arbitrarily. Let the line organization help formulate what the decision ought to be. Then the line manager has the responsibility not only of accepting the decision, but also of being sure that it is correctly transferred to the next group of people that have to do something with it.

Q. What is the correct time to transfer a project from your basic group into a divisional laboratory, particularly when you are dealing with individuals?

A. Since there are usually several groups involved to different degrees, there would be a number of different approaches and certainly different opinions as to this timing.

Q. Have you considered appointing a single project leader to cut across administration lines to keep that project clean and to solve all the red tape involved?

A. Yes, we do that occasionally. The thought flashed through my mind as Professor Bright spoke earlier this morning. We had a situation in our company nine or ten years ago where it was fairly clear to some of us in the senior management that we were going to have to change our method of assembly of radio sets and television sets to an alarming degree. Here was a case where the inventions were not of major significance, yet we just had to get a new idea accepted. What we did was to create a whole new group of people who had the specific job of organizing that transition. They developed the appropriate factory equipment. They worked with the engineering fellows to show them how they would have to build the product under the new conditions. They bought the new production equipment, and so forth. After the job, which took about three years, was completed they were disbanded and put on other things. Here was a case where we simply had to do it that way. More normally, however, we try to keep the work as relevant as possible to the current product they are working on.

Sometimes you've got to arrive at an early basic decision as to where a new technology that will affect the future of two of our line divisions is going to go. In one case, I have had several meetings, and I have also scheduled meetings between the technical people where I am not present. I have deliberately kept away from it, but I have seen to it that there was someone there who acted informally as a chairman to develop understanding between, say, three different divisions as to just what this technology is and where it is likely to go. Now it won't be very long before there will be a common understanding among those people, and they themselves will come to an unofficial opinion as to which division it should go to. They'll begin to see how, if it were done that way, the other two can get the things that they want out of it.

When that thinking has begun to crystallize, then I'll start working on the other side of the problem. I'll begin to get the fellows who do the business planning in those areas together. I'll probably bring some of the technical people in to give them seminars on what is likely to happen. When that groundwork has been prepared, it is my intention to get together with the senior managers of those groups for a talk which I will present. The president of my concern and I will apparently make the decision; but, in fact, all we will be doing is to put the final stamp of approval on a decision which has already been formulated down at the working level. And if it isn't accepted down there, and if they haven't had a part in it, they aren't going to do it right anyway.

APPRAISING THE EFFECTS OF THE TECHNOLOGICAL STATE OF THE ART ON THE CORPORATE FUTURE

S. W. HERWALD

S. W. HERWALD

Vice President – Research
Westinghouse Electric Corporation
Pittsburgh, Pennsylvania

Dr. Herwald graduated as a mechanical engineer from Case School of Applied Science and holds an M.S. in Engineering and a Ph.D. from the University of Pittsburgh. His career with Westinghouse began after graduation, and has continued through engineering and management activities in the Special Products Development Division. From 1952 through 1958 he was manager of the Air Arm Division of Westinghouse and in 1959 was appointed Vice President-Research. He is author of numerous technical articles in the field of servomechanisms and control systems and computers. His duties have embraced wide experience in the translation of technical control concepts and research results into effective equipment.

Appraising the Effects of the Technological State of the Art on the Corporate Future

Much has been said and written about the knowledge explosion of the past decade and about the rapid changes in our technology. I was amused recently to read an illustration which General Holzman, of the Air Force Cambridge Research Laboratories, used to show the futility of trying to keep abreast of the technical literature. He posed this hypothetical case: Imagine a chemist who can read 30 languages fluently at a rate of four papers per hour. Further suppose that on January 1, 1959, he began to read all the papers of just chemical interest alone which where published in 1958. If he read continuously for 40 hours per week, by January 1, 1960, he would have found himself 10 years behind in his reading!

Now I think this example pretty well points up the problem, although we in corporate management are not faced with exactly the same type of frustration. It is true that much of the new recorded knowledge is intellectually interesting, and contributes as basic building blocks upon which still further gains of knowledge may be achieved. We at Westinghouse also believe that to truly comprehend the value of new knowledge in areas of interest to us, we must participate in the generation of that knowledge — in other words, do basic research in areas of interest. At any given time, however, a large part of the new knowledge is of little practical significance to industry. We in the manufacturing business have an interest in all new knowledge in our fields, but we have a focused interest in that knowledge which contributes to the better attainment of a desirable function, or which presents an opportunity for accomplishing a heretofore unrealized functional performance. This selection is our concern if our companies are to show the continuing profits which make possible the research leading to additional new knowledge.

It is therefore important to try to select the areas and combinations of new knowledge that have the highest probability of contributing to profitability. I should like to consider with you today some of the techniques which, although admittedly crude, I believe can enhance our chances of being successful in this selection process.

At the outset I should remark that it is extremely difficult to choose the right areas of new knowledge for future exploitation, and I am certain no one has a sure-fire formula for predicting the absolute success of such selections. Actually what we are trying to do is to increase the chances of our being successful. What I will talk about today will be more of the approach to the problem rather than the actual solution. However, even that simplification is likely to become involved, as we shall presently see.

*   *   *   *   *

First, I should like to discuss some general considerations which should be taken into account. In terms of the present, it is important that we think of the basic nature of the business we are in and of the types of new technology which might upset it. For example, if we are in the restaurant business, we might well consider the effects of vending-machine developments on the way we conduct our marketing. At first we might think that vending machines would have a detrimental effect, but on looking further we possibly could find that what appeared to be a threat is really an opportunity for growth.

In terms of the future, we must frequently ask the question: "What kinds of new business might the corporation want to enter, and what types of technology would be required?" Extending our previous example, we might actually decide that we should set up restaurants using vending machines and even go into the business of manufacturing the machines we need. The latter would perhaps demand some new development, such as better automatic controls for the machine, and this in itself might discourage our entry into this field. In any event, the thinking has taken into account things as you really visualize they will be — not as they were or not as you would like them to be.

Before I proceed, I should like to bring out what may seem to be an obvious consideration, but it is one that is really basic to the whole discussion which follows. Just accomplishing the technology necessary for the performance of a functional job means very little unless we have thought about whether it will *really influence* what people want. Furthermore, we must ask ourselves,

"How *many* people will want the device or service that the technology makes possible?" In other words, we are saying, "Suppose the technology is successful — then what?"

Another question to be answered has to do with probability of success due to the selection of various areas for exploitation. To do this we must first survey the relevant fields of science for those areas of new knowledge that have the highest probability of contributing to profitability. Estimating this probability is at best difficult and requires a detailed look at several factors.

The primary consideration is whether the new information will provide the technical feasibility to meet some market need. Another way of arriving at a useful plan is to look initially at a market need, and then search the areas of new technology to see whether the technical feasibility to match that need actually exists or will be forthcoming. Once these two factors have been established — that is, the market need and the technical feasibility — a hard look must be given at time, cost, and strategy. An estimate must be made of the time required to complete the necessary research and development, together with the cost of this effort. Finally a definite plan must be made to relate the preceding factors to the competitive picture.

* * * * *

Let us look briefly at some of the effects of technological uncertainty. When a new field appears to be opening up because of some new scientific development, the decision must be made on the extent of the corporation's participation in the new field. Sometimes the area is one that you cannot afford *not* to do something about.

Often a new development will make possible several ways of doing a functional job. For example, you probably have read and heard about the efforts of Westinghouse and other firms in the area of direct energy conversion. This work is aimed at finding more efficient means of producing electricity than we are using today. Our better understanding of certain physical effects and our increased knowledge of materials have allowed us to proceed on four new methods of producing electric power — thermoelectricity, thermionics, fuel cells, and magnetohydrodynamics.

If we assume that defensive strategy demands that some program be maintained, two choices exist: First, if you are convinced that you have a clear view of the future, you bet all your chips on one method, and you try to get your new product on the market ahead of the competition. Obviously the element of risk associated with this choice is quite high, but the payoff can be correspondingly high.

Second, if, because of a more obscure vision, you choose to play it somewhat safer, you try to keep some activity going in all areas until you are able to see clearly where to put the emphasis. This essentially has been my company's choice in the direct-energy-conversion field. Tentatively we have preselected two of the methods as being the most promising and have allocated most of our energy-conversion effort to these; at the same time, the other two are kept going, at a rate sufficient to understand all of the implications of technical advances in these cases. At some point in the future we may decide to shift the emphasis from one method to another, depending upon the changes in the technology.

Another important factor related to technological uncertainty has to do with timing. Sometimes the key question is just when the state-of-the-art advancement will pay off. There may be no doubt that the work will eventually be profitable, but the efficient use of a company's resources demands that the benefits be foreseeable. Even if an idea is technically sound, if it requires 100 years to become profitable, we would have to reject it.

With these preliminary considerations in mind, I should like to turn now to some of the techniques that contribute to the probability of future profitability. The first is timing. In a given field of technology, a spectrum of development rates may be assumed on the basis of the present state of the art and the predicted future advances. (Figure 1) A whole family of curves can be assumed. Rate A can be immediately ruled out because the effort required to reach the market at the time indicated is impossibly large. Likewise Rate X is also eliminated because it is so slow that the effort never catches up and misses the market entirely. Now the decision-making function comes clearly into play because we have to decide which of these remaining curves our effort must assume. Rate B, for example, may mean that we require 50 scientists and engineers to meet the schedule. The men needed to achieve Rate C, on the other hand, may be only 30 but the number of years to complete the R & D task has now increased from 5 to 8. We must

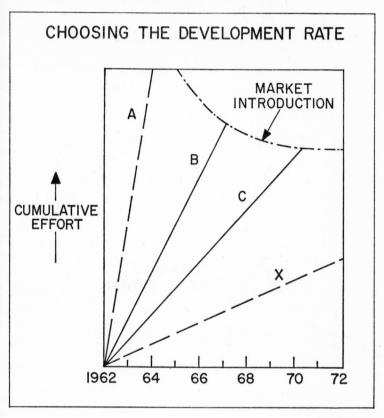

Figure 1

further factor in the competition and decide which of the curves will allow us to get the item to the marketplace early enough to achieve the premium profits that occur in the beginning phase of a new product's life cycle. This is the period (Figure 2) that we are most interested in.

❊ ❊ ❊ ❊ ❊

Still another question we may ask is concerned with the evolutionary change in the company's business picture which might be brought about by some new technology. One consideration that is sure to have an increasingly profound effect on the character of many businesses is the so-called functional approach in the design

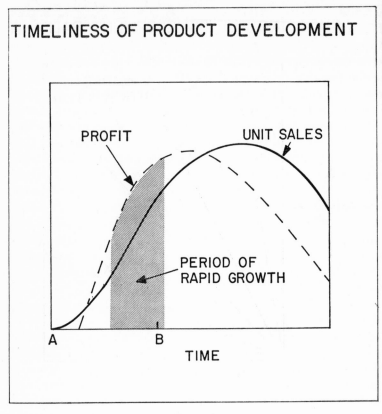

Figure 2

of new products. Here we think first of the customer's need; then we try to devise some way of using our new technical knowledge to bring about the functional performance desired by the customer.

Now what I mean by functional performance is this: In the past we have always thought of the customer's need for a single item. That is, we have supplied the housewife with a refrigerator when what she has actually needed has been refrigeration. We have marketed a heating or a cooling system when the customer has needed environmental conditioning — the function, not the piecemeal addition of more and more boxes.

A good example of what can be done in the functional area is what my company calls "molecular electronics." You have perhaps read about the advances of several concerns in this area and the possible change projected for radios, television, and other electronic equipment. I should like to take a few minutes to describe this area in enough detail that we can see the effects of our new technology and of the use of the functional approach.

First, I must review a little of the background involved so that we can understand how this product came about and how the technological state of the art affected its development. This example will show the profound changes that are possible from the standpoint of future corporate business. Let's go way back to about 1915, when the DeForest invention of the three-element vacuum tube first allowed us to obtain amplification in an electronic circuit. Various additions were subsequently made to improve the vacuum tube, but one limitation prompted the development, in 1948, of the transistor. This device does not have the filament, or heater, found in the vacuum tube, which means much longer life and that many more transistors than vacuum tubes can be contained in a given volume because there is less problem of removing the heat dissipated by the device. Following the transistor invention, the development of semiconductor junction devices opened up a new era of electronic progress. From this development came the microcomponent assembly, which was a means of using the same basic parts of an electronic circuit but making all the elements — transistors, resistors, and capacitors — smaller and lighter. Such a technique was of greatest importance to the military, for they were becoming increasingly concerned with packing more and more electronic equipment in less and less space. Aircraft and missile work demanded this approach.

The trouble was, however, that while the individual components were being made smaller, our electronic systems were becoming more complex. For example, the B-29 of World War II had something like 1,000 electronic components; today's B-58 requires almost 100,000 such components. This means a great reliability problem because of the possibility of failure of each component and of each connection between components.

So a new approach was needed, and that is exactly what we have in molecular electronics. By this technique we replace the many components and connections in an electronic circuit with a single piece called a molecular block.

Figure 3 shows one of our blocks — a video amplifier — pictured next to a dime for size comparison. The conventional video amplifier has many pieces in it, and each of these elements can be a source of failure. Not only that, but in the usual video amplifier there are numerous soldered connections, and each connection is also a source of failure.

Now let's consider the approach used in molecular electronics. Actually, the reduction in size is merely a byproduct of this concept. The big advantage is in the functional approach to the problem. In other words, we are not thinking in terms of connecting resistors, capacitors, and transistors to achieve some desired electronic purpose. Rather we are thinking of the over-all function that is involved and how a single piece of semiconductor material

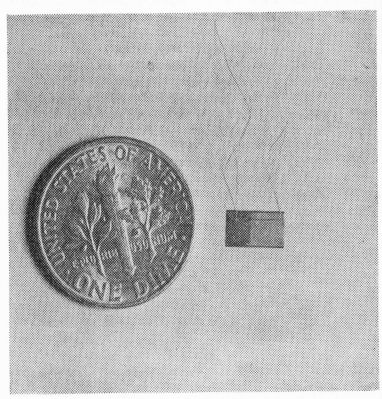

Figure 3

can be modified to produce the combined effect of amplification. This we are learning to do by controlling the distribution of impurities in the semiconductors used and by various methods of slotting, etching, and shaping.

The development of the molecular block has been a systematic integration of separate but related technologies. We found ourselves with the necessary knowledge of the properties of semiconductors and with the proper materials, and we were faced with the pressing need of improving the over-all reliability of complex electronic equipment. So we simply attacked the problem from the functional viewpoint.

I think you will agree that changes of concept such as that illustrated by molecular electronics may have a decided influence on the corporate business picture.

* * * * *

Let's look now at a consideration that is somewhat akin to the picture we dealt with a few minutes ago. I'm speaking of exploration of the unconventional. This area will, I believe, become increasingly important in the years ahead. More and more products will come from such functional considerations, and the amazing rate of our technological advancement will allow us to produce what would be termed today as the "unconventional."

Suppose we assume that, by our unconventional approach in molecular electronics, we can develop a complete line of equipment that is today unheard-of. We might put the size and reliability advantages to use in such products as portable general-purpose computers that would be practical for use in the home by the consumer.

What could such a computer do? Well, it could turn our TV on and off at the right time, according to our viewing habits; it could take phone calls when we were out and record the message; it could regulate the thermostat on our environmental conditioning system. It could perform the accounting function for the family budget, and it could tell us at any given instant how much our bank account was overdrawn and how much beyond our means we were living.

Before you become amused at my assumption of a home computer, let me give you a statement reported by O. E. Dunlap, in *The Future of Television*, a book published in 1947. As you may recall, television was first unveiled to the general public at the World's Fair of 1939. Here is Dunlap's quotation, which he said was made by many people: "Television is a social novelty, a millionaire's toy, and there are not many millionaires left in the United States; not enough, anyway, on which to build an industry. It's the masses that are the lifeblood of radio, and that *goes* for television."

It is interesting to look at the rapid rise of the manufacturing market for this device. (Figure 4) In 1946 the dollar volume due to production of sets was something like a million dollars. But look at the figure for 1950 — it had jumped to over 2 billion dollars per year. This rise was due not only to the customer need for this device but also to the changes in our technology — including manufacturing techniques — which were brought into play. In 1947 Dunlap said the television had been labeled a "50 million dollar *if.*" That was the amount of money that, prior to 1947, had been spent in research and development, and this laid the foundation for what is now a billion dollar industry. Today many outstanding developments are seen in this product, which as you may know, is found in 90% of the American homes.

Getting back to our home computer, let's suppose that 20 years after its introduction practically every home has one — just as is the case with TV.

Now with the acceptance of this new product, my company's business might again be radically changed. We might find it more profitable, for example, to devote a larger share of our effort to low-power-level electronics. It is easy to see that this segment of our business could be doubled if we were to come up with an unconventional approach, such as a home computer employing molecular-electronic circuitry.

The point that I have been trying to make is that one product of our rapidly changing technology can very easily alter the corporation's business emphasis. Consequently we should pay particular attention to the new technology pertaining to lines we don't really know about. The unconventional will play a big part in the future of all of our companies.

* * * * *

The last technique I want to talk about is what I like to think of as pacing. Any company — large or small — must think in

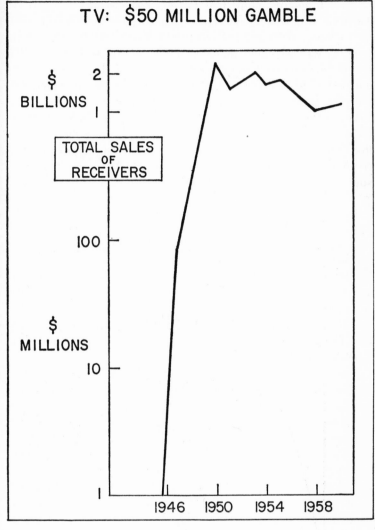

Figure 4

terms not only of today, but also of tomorrow. Long-range planning is necessary if the business is run according to principles of good management.

This means that we have to consider calmly and systematically many facets of any new technology, as I mentioned earlier, and we have to guard against being overly responsive in the various stages of a development. Here is a curve of accomplishment versus time. (Figure 5) Note that if we view this curve from point A, we are likely to be over-enthusiastic because at that time the development appears sure to reach the desired threshold. Our urge is to rush out and tie up more capital in new facilities to exploit this technology. However, we may subsequently suffer certain reverses, and now we view the curve from point B. Here again we have an intuitive feeling, but this time in the opposite direction. Now it looks as if we have the wrong approach, and we are thinking in terms of getting out of the business altogether. Now our feeling is one of pessimism.

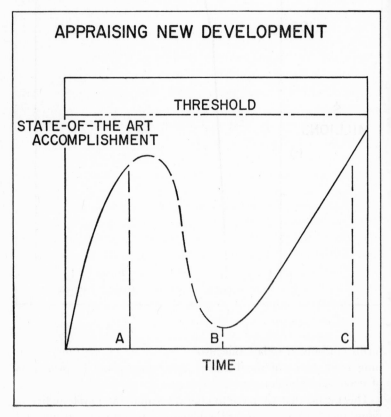

Figure 5

In actual fact, however, it may turn out that both viewpoints, although perfectly understandable at the time, were wrong. The curve could finally take the desired slope and point C assures the attainment of the threshold.

It frequently happens that the first spark of success is enough to set off a fire in the manager's imagination, especially if the scientists under his direction were responsible for the initial glimmer of light produced by some basic discovery. In theory all possible sorts of applications can be proposed, and indeed many may prove technically feasible. But there is much to be done between the proof of feasibility and the appearance of a product on the market.

On the other hand, it is easy for a manager to throw up his hands when he reaches the low point on the curve. This is a normal reaction.

But the pacer is the one who is there when the development really pays off. His attitude has been unemotional and carefully calculated. He does not rely on past experience. He looks at the data. From his objective review of the facts of the matter, he systematically appraises the chances of success offered by the technology at hand.

In the long run, he is the one who makes the most of his research and development resources.

* * * * *

To summarize, I have attempted to show that the real objective from the corporate viewpoint is to enhance the probability of bringing technology, in various combinations of the old and the new, to the point of solving the functional needs of our society. Therefore it becomes apparent that, to the entire mass of new technology — which is exploding at an exponential rate — we can profitably apply the following means of improving our chances of success:

First, choose those areas of the technology that bear on a particular functional performance.

Second, time the program of development so that the new product reaches the market soon enough to reap the premium profits that are possible only in the early phase of a new product's life.

Third, pay particular attention to those technologies that are likely to change the *mode* of the business we're in.

Fourth, think in terms of the new technology related to the lines which we really don't know about.

Finally, determine the pace that must be set and do it by making an unemotional, objective assessment of the facts.

By using such an approach to the problem, we can perhaps make a more intelligent appraisal of the effects of the technology on the corporate future and increase our batting average on profitable successes.

Q. You said that one must not let a current wave of disenchantment discourage us too much. We should evaluate the data at hand. Now how do you evaluate the data when the negative curve you've just shown is at its maximum value?

A. I'll tell you how we've been doing it. We try to isolate what is the critical technical thing that is holding us up. Then we concentrate our work in that area, aimed at what we call a critical experiment that will determine in a more scientific way whether we really can get past that hurdle or not.

Q. You evaluate differently from that which you said you were going to do. Is that right?

A. What we're saying is that you've got to isolate — you've got to arrange to get new data on which to make the evaluation. Right? You don't immediately wring your hands and say all is lost. On the other hand, once you've decided that something is a perpetual motion machine that you haven't been able to recognize in the disguise, you'd better get off that bandwagon in a hurry.

Q. Perhaps in the manager's eyes the curve in Figure 5 would mean the most by recognition of the whole situation as it exists in the data. Management does not qualify these decisions as much as we would care to qualify them.

A. Yes. This is the point I was trying to make. If you really look at the facts, it doesn't look like that wavy curve in Figure 5, because we've got a rough rule that it costs approximately ten times as much to exploit an idea on which the feasibility has been established as it does to establish the feasibility. So, if you want to accept this, it is well worth doing your homework on establishing the feasibility before you go tearing off on the big venture.

Q. Dr. Herwald, what technique have you developed for making a decision when you are dealing with something beyond your own technical comprehension and technical proof, and two equally respected and accomplished "experts" offer you diametrically opposed opinions as to whether it can be done or not?

A. That one is easy. You get them to agree on what experiment will show which one is right and which one is wrong. Let them run that experiment which they mutually agree will distinguish the difference between their approaches. It usually winds up that neither one is wholly right or wholly wrong. In most cases they wind up deciding that some third route is the best one to take.

Q. How do you decide which form of a scientific breakthrough you're going to exploit? For instance, in your firm's scientific activities you create new materials or new equipment, or perhaps new systems. What combination of these things will you try to accomplish?

A. That's a complex problem. I'll just give you the outline of it. Basically, we try in the broadest sense to put ourselves in the ultimate customer's shoes. I think if we put ourselves in the intermediate customer's shoes, we might sometimes be fooled. But if you put yourself in the ultimate customer's shoes, you can build up a hypothetical system for each possibility. In other words, the ultimate customer is you or I either in our plants or at home, buying electrical energy. For each alternative product you can hypothecate a system that gives the ultimate customer the electric power that he wants to use. It turns out that some product approaches have fundamental advantages that look as though they're worth pursuing, and others look as though they have fundamental limitations that aren't worth pursuing.

Q. Some will make sense in light of probability and market possibilities?

A. Well, first essentially we try to establish feasibility of what we can do technically. What size blocks are economical? What would the rough cost be per kilowatt installed? What would the operating cost be? All the key questions that would determine whether somebody would really want this. Remember at your end of your power line you probably couldn't care less whether the 60-cycle that showed up there at 220 volts came from a thermionic generator or a backscratcher that did it by static electricity. What you're really interested in is that, when you turn your lights on, you get the right power at the right voltage.

Q. You have a choice in selling materials, conversion devices, subsystems, and all that. In power conversion, you can sell more power stations; you can sell generators, or you can sell the pieces that go into television. How do you decide if you can do all three?

A. I can't answer that one because in some cases we do all three, in some cases we do two, and in some cases we do one. It comes back to what was mentioned before; you've got to take into account the kind of marketing structure you already have built into the company. How do you reach the customers that are going to use these things? If we decide to go into the sale of materials, this is a different set of sales organizations and a different kind of sales contact from those selling apparatus to the utilities. We try to decide whether there is enough business in this one material that would come up in, say, thermionics, to warrant setting up this kind of sales organization, licensing others, or whatever else our strategy might be. This is what I meant when I said you've got to have an explicit strategy of what you're going to do.

Q. And the strategy might indicate two or three choices?

A. Right. You try to do the one that offers you the best advantage of getting the most out of what you put in.

Q. (Mr. Smith) May I add a little bit to that? I think it's not unlikely that Westinghouse and Philco have essentially the same technical capabilities in this particular area that you're talking about. But the companies are quite different in their general structure. Westinghouse can depend on public utilities since they sell a lot to them; our company can't. Given exactly the same subsystem capability, we would decide not to push the thing and Westinghouse would decide to do it because of the . . . technological relationships and marketing strategy.

Q. What I was getting at was that in making this kind of decision, it does not have to be made by some corporate group who looks at the whole company and makes the decision. Can the decision be made by some individual? Or does he have too limited a viewpoint?

A. We actually have a group preparing the ground information from which management can pick out alternatives. The group happens to be made up of marketing, our central lab people, and the manufacturing people. Manufacturing is one thing we haven't mentioned too much here because it generally happens to be the third thing we consider. Do we have the manufacturing capability? Sometimes this will be the overriding question and will establish that we don't want to go on. But we do have this group which says that from this particular combination, this strategy would lead to the highest probability of success.

Q. I think you left out the biggest obstacle that's back of it all — the capital control aspect. The firm must use capital to exercise its greatest strength and this decides which way the thing should go.

A. Yes, but that's in the plan that is proposed. In other words, how many dollars is it going to take us to get there; when are we going to get there; what are we going to deliver; and what is our market going to be?

Q. You superimpose capital control on individual plans which are actually capable of being followed?

A. Yes, the worst thing you can do is to not have that agreed upon in advance. To have a project that's successful come to a large capital expenditure decision point and then have somebody decide "we don't have it" is the greatest waste of good effort and usually demoralizes the people involved. The capital decision must occur at the same time we embark upon development research and the availability of capital assured at successful check points.

Q. What do you mean by pacing?

A. Pacing means to really evaluate where you are when someone comes in and says, "I've got a red hot idea. It's going to revolutionize everything." Sit down and really calculate, then, what he knows and what he doesn't know. I think you'll find that the curve in Figure 5 really isn't as high as he said. It's only part way up there. When you look at the low point he described, you'll find out that this is only the way he's told it to you. He has fewer problems now than he had before, but he recognizes them more clearly than he did before. That was what I intended by pacing. Because if those negative points were really the facts, then you probably would never have gotten to where you are.

TECHNOLOGICAL PLANNING AND MISPLANNING

MISPLANNING

M. P. O'BRIEN

M. P. O'BRIEN

Dean Emeritus, College of Engineering
University of California
Berkeley, California

Dean O'Brien received his Bachelor of Science degree from Massachusetts Institute of Technology in 1925. From then until 1927 he was on the staff of the Experimental Station at Purdue University. From 1927 through 1928 he was a Freeman Scholar of the American Society of Civil Engineers, engaged in the study of hydraulics in Sweden. He served successively as professor, chairman of the Department of Mechanical Engineering, and Dean, College of Engineering, at the University of California from 1928 to 1959. During 1947-1949 he was on leave from that university to act as Director of Research and Engineering at Air Reduction Company. He has been a consulting engineer with the General Electric Company since 1949 on such subjects as engines, nuclear powered aircraft, missiles and space vehicles, and electronic systems. During the last ten years he has participated in and observed the planning of many technological efforts.

Technological Planning and Misplanning

The legitimate and primary objective of a business should be to make a profit. More specifically, the primary objectives of a business should be (a) to make a profit now, and (b) to take action now to assure profitable operations in the future. There are, of course, exceptions to this statement as in the case of development projects in government laboratories or work undertaken by industry at a nominal fee for special reasons.

There are many facets of the second objective — "to assure profitable operations in the future" — and these notes deal with only one, namely, the development of new products and new product lines as an essential component of continued success in a business engaged in the manufacture and sale of technical products.

Some Definitions

The words "research" and "development" have been used together so generally as to imply that R & D is a single activity. In reality, there is a fundamental difference between them — in objectives, in their relationship to the needs of society, and in the viewpoint and intellectual characteristics of their practitioners.

A problem of semantics has resulted from the tendency toward "inflation" of terms — drafting is called design; design is called development; development is called research; and true research must be modified for clarity and called "basic research." For the purposes of this paper — and not as an attempt at semantic precision — the key words will be used in the following sense:

"Science" embraces both the accumulated knowledge of the physical world and the work of extending this knowledge.
"Research" describes the process through which new facts and relationships in nature are discovered.
"Engineering," like science, has a broad connotation which makes simple and precise definition difficult. In this context, it may be described as the process of designing, developing, and building specific equipment and systems — a bridge, an engine, a radar, an electric power system.

"Development" describes a phase of design in which the objective sought is beyond the current state of the design art and in which novel design concepts are evaluated and improved by experimentation, usually guided and evaluated by analysis.

The distinction made is that scientific research seeks facts and generalizations, while engineering development is directed toward specific tangible results — ultimately to be embodied in hardware.

These notes deal with development work and not with scientific research.

International Competition

The United States must pay for its imports of raw materials, fuel, foreign travel, special equipment, and other items by the export of finished goods — which must compete in a world market on the basis of their quality and cost. Clichés about the importance of research to the economy are so commonplace that brief comment seems to be in order here.

The results of basic research are available worldwide almost without delay or censorship. There may be areas of science that are held secret in some countries, but for the most part secrecy is applied only to the advances in technology. Furthermore, science of itself does not produce results which are directly useful. A scientific discovery may provide the principle underlying a product having immense economic or military importance, but there remains the difficult task of translating the solution in principle to a solution in hardware.

A new and useful product enjoys an advantage in the international market place; foreign competitors, however, can — and will — copy the design if the selling price gives them inducement to do so. Development work is a difficult way for an individual or a company to earn a living in the domestic economy, even with the protection of an effective patent system. It is no longer possible for a nation to achieve such superiority in new product development as to support its import requirements on the profits from novelty alone.

Except for periods of temporary advantage due to novelty, competition among nations in the sale of technical products will hinge on quality and price. Encouragement and support of basic research and skill in the development of new products are essential to technological leadership, but they alone do not assure the income to pay for necessary imports. Sustained production of goods that are competitive in the international market in quality and price requires analysis and action now in many quarters.

The preceding comments are not intended to imply that the nation's research effort should be lessened; it should be increased in the area of truly basic research. However, effective development work and production at competitive costs are equally important to our national position.

The United States is spending approximately 12 billion dollars a year on research and development — a not inconsequential fraction of our gross national product. Most of this sum is devoted to development projects. The effectiveness of this work in developing new products — industrial and military — will be a major factor in the military-economic war in which this country is engaged.

Conflict Between Profits Now and Profits in the Future

An accounting department casts up statements of sales and manufacturing cost, of taxes, amortization, capital charges, and other factors measurable in dollars, and reports a profit or loss. What such profit and loss statements omit is an appraisal of the concurrent loss or gain in other assets not measurable in dollars; among these is the store of potential and actual new technological products which *may* produce profits in the future. The more novel and the more potentially profitable a new product is, the more visionary and impractical it appears when first proposed. The present value of future profits from a novel idea, not yet demonstrated, is difficult to express in terms which a qualified accountant would include in the profit and loss statement. Unfortunately, the negative side of new product development — the cost — is measurable by the accountants in terms everyone can understand.

Development work reduces profits now in the *hope* of sustaining profits in the future, but there can be no certainty that these hoped-for profits will materialize. Merely spending money on staff and facilities, and on design and testing, may produce only interesting but unprofitable results. Effectiveness in assessing the state of technology, in selecting potentially profitable products, in estimating the market available and the timing, in planning and executing a development program, in forecasting the manufacturing cost in production, and in introducing the new product, all require knowledge, experience, intuition, and much luck. The managers of a technical business are understandably hesitant about cutting deeply into present profits to support development work because they face many uncertainties, including not only the potential profitability of the product but also the capacity of their organization to achieve the desired results at acceptable cost in time to exploit the potential market.

The conflicting demands imposed by the need for present profits and for the assurance of future profits through new developments is reflected in attitudes within the organization. The operating units are responsible primarily for producing a profit *now* — and there is frequently a personal *financial* incentive toward maintaining current profits at as high a level as possible. The success of the development and design organization, however, requires that its efforts be supported at the expense of profits now; this group must argue for their needs, usually as a minority among the managers, offering only hopes in return for dollars. When business is good, their efforts are not regarded as crucial; when it is poor, they are too expensive.

The two extremes are, on the one hand, to spend nothing on product improvement and new product development and to exploit the existing product line to the limit; on the other, to apply the entire net income to development work. As products and product lines go through their life cycle from exciting novelty to maturity and ultimate extinction, the balance between profits and expenditures for development work should change; with luck, the management adjusts this balance to optimize present and future profits.

Defense industries face problems of financing development work which differ in detail from those of a commercial business, but the fundamental problem is the same, namely, that resources available now must be allocated so as to assure new products in the future. Since these companies are more in the position of offering technical competence than of selling a developed product, their advanced work should stress the strengthening of their position in science and technology, in the techniques of design and development, and in unique development facilities. Under cost-sharing of development work, the situation of the defense contractor approaches that of normal competitive enterprise.

The decision regarding how much to spend from current income to *develop profitable products for the future* must be made in terms of *this* business at *this* time; there is no generally valid formula to be applied. Companies competing in the same field of technology may have sound reasons for different decisions in this respect — and these several courses of action may all be successful.

The Growth of a Technology

We have all witnessed the introduction, growth, and maturity of new technologies: the internal combustion engine and the automobile, electric power, photography, synthetic fibers, and many others. This characteristic cycle has been shortened in recent years. Progress as a function of time, measured by dollars spent, by number of workers, by number of technical publications, or in any other representative manner, can be represented by an S-curve in which four phases of growth can be distinguished:

1. *Invention or concept.* The greater the ultimate value of the idea, the more fantastic the idea seems when first proposed; once disclosed, other means of achieving the same end are conceived and tried. Feasibility studies and experiments show promise but unacceptable performance. The state of related science and technology is frequently controlling, especially in materials.

2. *Rapid growth.* If the idea is sound, one or more designs appear which are made to work. Capital becomes available for growth. Many competitors take the field and the concept is refined, simplified, reduced in cost, and production increases rapidly in volume. Competition in ideas sifts out the best combination of technique, materials, and performance. Income from sales permits increased development efforts and refinement of product.

3. *Consolidation and approach to maturity.* The number of competing concepts is reduced as some prove superior to others; the number of competitors is decreased as the weaker ones, usually pursuing inferior concepts, drop out or are absorbed.

The winning design or designs have been established; manufacturing costs and sales promotion receive the main attention.
4. *Maturity.* Improvements in the product are minor, occur at increasing intervals, and are relatively expensive for the gain achieved. The market is saturated. A few competitors remain.

This cycle of events is well known. It is described here because this changing environment should influence decisions regarding the strategy to be followed in developing new products and the decision regarding resources to be committed for this purpose. In the early phase, the profits may be large but so are the risks, and the casualties are numerous. The risks may be limited by holding off until later phases and then "buying in" through purchase of designs, patents, or going companies. It is difficult to assess the current status of a maturing technology — and what seems to be an approach to maturity may be altered by an innovation — but there are symptoms and trends which are indicative. In the mature phase, the momentum of usage and of heavy investment deters abrupt and drastic change; the innovator in these areas must be prepared for a costly and time-consuming effort to supplant the old concept with a new one.

The Evolution of a Development Project

Development projects, large or small, major innovations or minor improvements, follow the same sequence of steps, which are described below as a straightforward sequence but are in reality a series of approximations, with feedback from subsequent steps to refine the concepts and assumptions made earlier. Furthermore, the relative effort which must be devoted to each step will vary with the novelty of the design concept. These steps are as follows:

1. *A technical-economic objective* (or a technical-military objective) is identified, a task which involves the interplay of what is possible and what is needed; of costs and benefits; of requirements and capabilities. Will the benefits justify the costs? What benefits? What costs?

   If the objective is extremely novel, as were radar and the atomic bomb, the first question to be answered is whether or not the desired result is physically possible. Scientific knowledge and mathematical skill are required to identify the key problems, to design critical experiments in order to obtain the necessary data, and to analyze the test results. After the question of physical possibility is answered, the feasibility and practicability can be analyzed and the objectives of a development program formulated in terms of one or more concepts which would, in principle at least, attain the objective; a design concept is created. The cost of the subsequent development program and the value of the product developed are influenced enormously by the quality of the work in this first phase. Hasty decisions to rush into hardware, before a firm scientific base is provided, is costly in money *and time.*

2. *Analysis of the design concept* to express the environmental conditions quantitatively and to specify the characteristics of the subsystems, the components, and the materials is the first step in a *preliminary design.* The basic concept is necessarily qualitative and schematic in form, and — although theoretically possible — may require conditions which are not practically achievable. For example, power from controlled nuclear fusion has been shown to be a possibility by idealized experiments but the pressures and temperatures required for the reaction are beyond those which can be contained by solid boundaries; various concepts for magnetic containment have been proposed and studied analytically and experimentally without conclusive results as yet.

This example is extreme in its degree of novelty, but all development projects are, in essence similar in that the objective cannot be achieved through the existing state of the design art—and one must proceed by concept, analysis, and test through *all* the areas of uncertainty until at least one solution is found for *every* problem. Analysis and test are not possible until a design concept has been created for each part and for the whole system or device.

Practical considerations which usually become important at this stage in a development project are the cost, the time required, and the probable performance. The cost of analysis and experiment in the preliminary design phase of an advanced project is not inconsequential, but it is small as compared with the amount necessary to proceed from this point to a working prototype. The sponsors of the project, whether in government or in industry, wish to limit their commitment by "definitizing" the program but the questions asked cannot be answered, even approximately, until the major uncertainties are resolved, and not conclusively until the prototype is tested. Judgment based on experience, intuition, and mutual confidence are essential to avoid an impasse at this point.

The preliminary design and the related developmental analysis and experimentation add enough to the existing state-of-the-art that a working prototype can be designed in detail.

3. *Detailed design* is the process by which instructions are prepared for the purchase of materials and parts, for the fabrication of components, and for assembly of the prototype. Frequently, detailed design is started in parallel with preliminary design, particularly when long lead-time items are involved, but the work is subject to constant correction and modification as the preliminary design evolves until the time arrives when the preliminary design in hand is judged to have a reasonable chance of doing the job; then comes the agony of freezing the design. From this point on, proposed improvements must be rejected if they cause delay — but they must be considered. The groups in preliminary design and development must inject their knowledge into the detailed design and, in the course of doing so, they conceive new and different approaches until they come to regard the design in progress, but not yet brought to test in a prototype, as an obsolete klunker — and it may be so if the project management is not discriminating. The most economical course of action usually is to carry the first design to test as quickly as possible and to accumulate improvements for an advanced version because the prototype test is likely to reveal many troubles which were not anticipated.

4. The *prototype* is put to test, redesigned to eliminate defects, retested, and, with luck, brought to an acceptable level of performance.

As a project proceeds through this sequence from concept to prototype test, the cost and the number of workers required in each step, and the number qualified for the work, increases greatly. Skill and thoroughness in developing the preliminary design will effect substantial reductions in the cost of the detailed design and the prototype test. One step is not more important than the others; they are all essential.

The preliminary and detailed design of a prototype requires choices of materials and components which will be difficult to change in the production version without excessive cost. Choices made by designers which had little effect on performance may affect production costs to a substantial degree.

The Project Versus the Functional Organization

When only one project is undertaken at a time, the problems of organization are relatively simple, but as the number of projects increases, the same scientific and engineering talents and the same technical services are required on several projects concurrently. A functional grouping of the organization — development, design, testing, computing, fabrication — may conserve manpower and make available to each project greater competence than would be available if each project were self-contained.

This reasoning about a functional organization has merit, and the principle can be applied successfully when the succession of projects involve only variations and improvements of a single concept. It is the engineering organization appropriate to a mature area of technology.

A novel concept cannot be developed through the medium of a functional organization. The statement is made categorically because the writer knows of no exceptions — a separate and autonomous group is essential — and it is important that this group control the budget as well as the technical work. The project group may be small and may call on a functional organization for many services, but it must at least be competent to carry through the preliminary design and establish quantitative subordinate objectives for the detailed design, to plan the component and prototype tests, and to evaluate the results of work done by others.

The Project Engineer

The individual who manages a development project must have the viewpoint of an engineer — a compelling interest in achieving the tangible end result with the least effort — whatever may be his education, his professional society membership, or his job description. Physicists, chemists, and mathematicians, as well as graduate engineers, have served successfully as project managers; in general, an engineer should be best qualified for this assignment provided that he qualifies in other respects. The starting point of a development project is a solution in principle; the end point is a solution in hardware. The requirement is to traverse the intervening distance at minimum cost and in minimum time.

Development work ranges in character from improvements of an established product to highly creative applications of recent scientific discoveries. Generalizations about the knowledge and experience of a project manager are difficult to formulate beyond the obvious requirement that he be familiar with the scientific principles and the analytical and experimental methods pertinent to his problem. He cannot be an expert in all the related fields, but he must know enough to recognize, and depend on, others who are really experts and to be decisive in avoiding interesting but unproductive scientific side issues. Advanced projects, especially those which require a team effort involving scientists, mathematicians, and engineers in the early phases, represent a particularly difficult problem of management because the engineers who have the production viewpoint and the managerial skill are frequently found to be lacking in the requisite knowledge of science and of the viewpoint of scientists. The scientist, on the other hand, is inclined to be satisfied with solution in principle and to view with distaste the plodding effort required to realize a design in hardware, especially when many attractive improvements have appeared after the design was frozen.

Nearly all major development projects pass through three or four managerial crises — usually resulting in a change of manager after much confusion, unhappiness and lost time. These situations arise as the result of circumstances which repeat themselves so often as to constitute a law of nature. Change is inevitable in management of a project for reasons discussed in the preceding paragraph. Individuals who are qualified by knowledge, originality, and experience to guide an advanced project through its formative stages of scientific exploration and feasibility and who aim the project toward a difficult but achievable target, are almost certainly not qualified to manage it much beyond this point; even if they were qualified and willing, their talent is so rare that it should be applied to other advanced efforts. Each phase of a project presents different major problems. The change of managers to meet these requirements should be an accepted, routine event, anticipated and carried out without disruption of work. Unfortunately, the inevitable change of manager is usually delayed until a crisis in performance, schedule, money, or personnel forces the issue, to the discredit of the outgoing project manager, when the basic fault was failure on the part of the higher management to recognize the symptoms early and to plan a replacement in time.

Large companies engaged in a diversified technical business have a better opportunity to change managers on development projects than do small ones. When the company is small, possibly coincident in scope with a single development, the problem is acute, because there is no objective means of appraising the situation and of choosing a replacement. The electronics industry, especially in some segments such as semiconductors, seems now to be suffering from the inability of many small companies, founded on the basis of a novel concept, to change their management emphasis to be compatible with the present phase of the technology and the effects of competition.

Pioneering work in a new area of technology must overcome so many obstacles — physical feasibility, hostile expert criticism, inadequate finances, market development, and so forth — that the successful director of such work must exhibit personal qualities which are rare and often annoying to others. Self confidence to the point of arrogance, single-minded dedication to the job, impatience with adverse criticism, and disregard of side effects and minor obstacles are characteristic of such individuals; the exacting task of executing a pioneering effort successfully seems not only to require these qualities but to accentuate and harden them. There have been exceptions to this generalization, but not many. Large technical-scientific organizations can, in principle, compensate for the scarcity of such individuals through group direction of the work and through changes in the director at appropriate times, but such organizations usually come into being after the pioneering work in a new field is over.

The successful pioneer in a new area of technology has confounded the skeptics who said that the idea would not work, or that it was of no value, or that it had been tried before unsuccessfully, and so forth; also, he has resisted the suggestions of supporters who urged delay to permit improvement. He has been forced by the obstacles inherent in such work to defend his chosen course of action — his compromise between performance, cost, and time — to defend it so consistently and vigorously that he comes to regard it as the best possible result, rather than as a practical compromise and consequently probably subject to improvement. For example, the firm of Boulton and Watt spent many years trying to persuade Parliament to limit steam engine pressures to the pressures then designed into engines because higher pressures were both unnecessary and unsafe. This phenomenon is accentuated in the case of the pioneers in a new field, but it is found to some degree among the ex-leaders of more prosaic development projects after they move on to other assignments. The objectives they sought were so novel and so difficult that they are often not receptive to suggestions for improvement or for development of a new concept which will supplant their work.

Large development organizations with many projects in progress concurrently have the same problems of communications and control that size brings to organizations of any type. Authority is concentrated but the knowledge necessary for the wise use of authority is diffuse. Control tends to concentrate on money considerations, and the short-range goals come to dominate the plans unless the decision-making process includes credible and well-rounded inputs regarding the less tangible long-range work.

Control of a Project

The over-all objectives of a development project have been discussed in general terms but a few more comments on the subject are appropriate as a background for a discussion of project control.

A development project is usually expensive — at least relative to the resources of the sponsor — and the results sought should be of such character as to justify the cost and the risk. Timidity can lead to products which are quickly obsolete and not worth developing. On the other hand, if the goal of the first prototype is so advanced as to require many innovations simultaneously, the time and cost may become so great before encouraging results are obtained that the project loses support. A recent example of this situation was the nuclear powered airplane for which the objective was an operational airplane capable of supersonic flight — and the longer this first objective was in force, the more difficult it was to back off to a more reasonable initial target. The first objectives should be difficult but achievable in reasonable time — and the prototype should be designed and put to test as quickly as possible after preliminary design indicates a reasonable chance of success.

The process of delineating objectives must be carried through to the subsystems, components, and all related tests in quantitative terms, with target dates and budgets for each. Without this type of coordination, the groups within a project can drift apart, each achieving a sound design but one not compatible with the over-all requirements. The tendancy to explore interesting side issues, to delay the matching of components at an interface, or simply to forget the quantitative objectives requires constant attention from the project management.

The lead time between concept and prototype test, the money involved, and the desire for early availability of the product require that important projects be *audited* at intervals, thoroughly and by an individual or group with the knowledge, experience, and time to probe all phases of the work. The stakes are too high and the chances for failure too great to assign the objectives and the resources and to await the final result. The project manager should welcome an audit as an independent check on his situation, and the higher management had better be wary when a project manager resists audit.

There are many observable check points in the course of a development at which predicted and actual progress can be compared, such as successful completion of tests of key components, of preliminary design, of release of drawings, and so forth. At some of these points, the rate of expenditure will increase rather abruptly and they are, in general, the effective points for thorough audit.

Control of the funds — and comparison of the expenditures with the degree of completion — is a complicated task. The accountants can supply the figures for expenditures and commitments, with some delay and some uncertainty over the indirect costs to be adjusted at the end of the year, but the sum required to complete the work can only be estimated. It is not uncommon for the project organization to estimate the percentage completion as roughly equal to the percentage of the budget spent — a happy situation until the money is gone and the work is incomplete.

Reappraisal, at intervals, of the work yet to be done and of the related costs is a more reliable approach, and this reappraisal is best accomplished in conjunction with a technical audit.

Development engineers dislike schedules because they imply that a problem will be solved — a "breakthrough" achieved — by a certain date. True, one cannot predict the date of an invention or of the desired results of analysis or experiment, but one can schedule the construction of facilities and components for test and the program of testing. It is an interesting fact that tight schedules are frequently met when taken seriously, sometimes with the aid of invention on schedule.

Development projects tend to cost an amount proportional to the elapsed time from concept to completion of prototype test. Data to prove this point are inadequate. At least, it always seems to follow that projects which overrun their time schedule overrun their budget. There are not many points on the other side of the target, but one major project with high priority was completed in three quarters of the estimated time at approximately three quarters of the estimated budget. When projects are slowed down for one reason or another and later resumed, the speed-up following resumption seems to absorb whatever was saved in the slack period. Economy seems to demand that development projects move ahead steadily at the maximum pace feasible, once a thorough preliminary design has been completed.

The Chance for Success

Some years ago the vice president for engineering of a large corporation, which had prospered on new products derived from its own research and development, summarized his company's experience as follows: Of the projects which were started in research and had gone far enough in company thinking to be given a separate listing and account number, only one in twenty was carried through to profitable production, and the elapsed time for the successful ones was, on the average, about eight years. Unsuccessful projects were, of course, terminated earlier. The risks were great but the gains were correspondingly high when the work was successful — and this particular company had the resources to take such risks. Corresponding figures have been cited for many other companies and industries.

Obviously, a company that could afford only one project at a time might wait many years to see its *research* and development program pay off with a winner. Even the largest companies cannot afford much truly basic research and none can depend on research alone as the source of new products. The risk — and usually the corresponding expectation of profit — can be reduced by starting development work nearer to the end product. Some companies have made a practice of buying foreign developments. Others confine their work to small advances within the existing state-of-the-art. Cost of manufacture, effectiveness of marketing, field services, availability of parts and overhaul facilities, can compensate for product novelty in sustaining a product line, but there is always present the hazard that a competitor will score a breakthrough and render the going product obsolete.

In some industries, companies have joined together to solve industry-wide problems through research and development programs sponsored by their trade association, usually acting through grants to universities, research institutes, and industrial laboratories. For the most part, these efforts are directed toward expanding applications of the common product but some seek to add knowledge basic to product design.

There must be a reasonable balance between income and the amount risked on new product development. The chance for success with whatever resources can be available, large or small, can be enhanced considerably by two means: (1) an effective organization devoted to technical-economic analyses, and (2) a systematic search for development ideas — a technical "scouting force." These items should be the first charges against the development budget, however small.

Technical-Economic Analyses

Appraisal of a proposed development project requires an objective technical-economic analysis, starting from the physical problems of development and manufacture and carrying through to sales and profit to provide management with a basis for decision. The expense of this work can be prohibitive if every proposal is subjected to complete analysis. Frequently, a single unfavorable factor may be decisive in eliminating a proposal; skill and intuition are essential to identify key elements of the problem early and thus avoid fruitless work. The process of decision making regarding the expenditure of funds on a novel development is a circular one. The questions raised usually cannot be answered without cost, possibly including the cost of experimentation, but the availability of funds hinges on favorable answers to these questions. A usual situation resulting from this impasse is that the technical proponents of an idea, who know little about markets and less about manufacturing costs, cast up a set of figures, usually optimistic, which covers only half the problem. Management suspects the figures — both because of their source and because of their rosy hue. It is amazing how many proposals, good and bad, in large and small development laboratories have remained suspended in this fashion for long periods, costing some money but making no progress, for lack of a mechanism of appraisal in which the management has confidence.

A series of approximations should characterize the technical economic analysis. If preliminary screening uncovers no absolute barriers and the first guess at profitability is encouraging, the proposal should be scrutinized in more detail to identify the problems requiring analysis or experiment. Work on these problems should provide the basis for subsequent appraisal, and so on, until the project is completed or abandoned.

Fifteen years of association with development work have strengthened my conviction that the minimum requirement for success in new product *acquisition* or *development* is competence in the technical-economic analysis of new product proposals. There are, to my knowledge, few organizations which do this type of work routinely and effectively.

The Search for Ideas

The preceding notes dealt with the appraisal of ideas for new products. Scouting for new ideas also needs attention to assure an adequate number for appraisal and selection and as insurance against being scooped by a competitor. Suggestions from internal and external sources, published literature, patent disclosures, and other sources do provide ideas in quantity, but possibly not of the quality needed. A scouting force — appropriate in size and caliber to the objectives sought — is a desirable adjunct to a development organization, possibly as a secondary assignment for some of the technical staff but on an ordered plan and with continuity of effort and contact.

These two suggestions may appear to be feeble approaches to

the problem of assuring a succession of new products, but, done effectively, they will yield a higher return per dollar spent than any other part of the development budget. Without this type of guidance, the development dollars may yield only interesting novelties, not profitable products.

By constantly searching for new product ideas and by appraising them objectively in the light of the company's circumstances — cash position, competition, know-how, and so forth — the risk assumed and the chance of success can be matched to the resources available so as to yield a profit now and assure a profit in the future.

Location in the Organization

The preceding section dealt with the nature of the decision regarding the support for development work; two major influences on this decision are the position of new product work in the structure of the organization and the age of the individuals having the authority to decide.

There is no one best place for development work in an organization; there are many feasible plans. The choice among them should be made on the basis both of the objectives sought and of the personalities involved. If the objective is to bring about small improvements in a product line and if the competitive position is strongly influenced by manufacturing costs, assignment of new product development to the manufacturing organization may be logical, but it is almost certain that novelty will not characterize the products evolved. There is always good reason to coordinate new product development with manufacturing, and placing both under the same manager may assure this result. If the developments are of an advanced nature, however, it is fatal to mix them in with a busy manufacturing group. If the market tends to define the need for a new product and if the technology required is well established, new product development may be effective in the marketing organization. Another combination, and the one most frequently used in adding to established product lines, is to combine engineering support of the going products with the engineering design and development of new products. This plan is effective when the new products are advanced versions in the established product line; a variation is a separate development organization but under the direction of the engineering manager. Going a step farther, there is the separate development organization reporting directly to the effective head of the business, whether a separate company or an autonomous division, and at the end of the sequence is the subcontracting of development work to outside research laboratories.

Each of these arrangements has advantages and disadvantages. Two or more of them may be followed in the same organization at the same time; different arrangements may be appropriate at different stages in the evolution of a technical business. There is no simple rule-of-thumb to follow in choosing among them, except possibly that the plan followed successfully in the past probably needs to be changed; this is true because every technical business moves inevitably toward maturity, requiring changing emphasis on new product development.

The interests, age, and personal characteristics of the different managers are sometimes a valid basis for the temporary assignment of new product development.

The Age of the Decision Makers

A delicate but important subject for discussion here is the relationship of the age of the decision makers on the character and scope of the development program.

Age brings experience and sound judgment. "Experience is the best teacher"; "Old men are wise and young men, impetuous"; and so on through all the clichés, aphorisms, and old wives' tales, which the elders have used for generations to restrain their juniors. True, judgment is important and years of experience should bring sound judgment. It is also true, unfortunately, that experience tends to be specific and to limit a man's vision to a narrow area. It is difficult to keep the mind open to innovations and to sift out of past experience those considerations which are pertinent to a new problem. The problem is particularly acute in men who have themselves carried through important development projects earlier in their careers. Development work is a tough way for an engineer or scientist to make a living. It is a young man's type of work, requiring discontent with the past and unbounded optimism for improvement. Uncertainty is their constant companion. Age brings a desire for stability, an impatience with constant change, and a weakening of the imagination and the creative urge. Obviously, top management must control this process and cannot let the development organization proceed without restraint, but in the process of decision making they must assess not only the experience of their advisers but their recent record of openmindedness about innovation.

Another problem of age — and one involving top management itself — is a lessened interest in new developments as the responsible managers approach retirement. This attitude is a human one, but it should be recognized and, if possible, circumvented. Age alone tends to produce this result, and it is reinforced by the realization, mostly subconscious, that money taken from profits now will not appear as profits from new products before retirement.

A personal experience illustrates the problem: Some years ago I was associated for a time with a company which was decentralized into about a dozen semi-autonomous operating units, each with a profit and loss statement and with almost complete authority over development expenditures. Two central development laboratories, each headed by a vice president, were dependent on the operating managers for their funds. During an extended automobile trip with these two vice presidents, I explored the extent to which the older managers supported their work. Retirement age in this company was 65 and, on the average, seven years elapsed between the first expenditures for development and profitable operations. There was plenty of time and they went back over the past two or three years in detail. They concluded that not one manager 59 years of age or older had backed them on new ventures; when they had received support from their divisions, it was only through pressure from the president.

Project Histories

There is much to be learned from the history of past projects — and particularly from those that failed because of problems of physical feasibility, financing, or markets. A large fraction of the much-respected folklore of the subject is wrong, and current decisions are influenced by a distorted view of the past. A simple quantitative summary of the objectives, the schedule achieved, the correspondence of results with objectives, the manpower, and the money, all as a function of elapsed time, would be helpful and can be compiled easily while the records are fresh. A second step, and one that would be most helpful to top management, is an intellectual history of the conception and execution of a project in which the interplay of viewpoints, personalities, policies, and financial and marketing restraints are re-counted. Who were for and who were against the project, and what were the reasons? Were the forecasts of performance, markets, costs, and schedule correct and how were these forecasts really made and by whom? Some such records may need to be kept confidential for a few years while they cool off but it is these reports which will be most helpful later. The audit reports made during the course of a project will be valuable appendices to such a record.

Q. You mentioned the desirability of making technological audits. Where do you find the technological auditors?

A. By borrowing for a limited period people who are knowledgeable in the field — from engineering, manufacturing, sales, finance, other projects — depending on the nature of the problem. Large organizations have enough qualified individuals who are between long-term assignments to staff a few audit teams. This assignment is good experience for prospective project engineers. A small continuing secretariat is helpful, but the team members should be changed frequently — with just enough carryover in membership to provide continuity in procedure and basic approach. There are matters of protocol affecting the groups audited which must be established and observed.

The results achieved by such audits depend primarily upon the extent to which the next higher level of command gives serious consideration to the conclusions.

Q. How can you control or plan development?

A. It is clear that one cannot schedule discovery or invention. However, once the development objective has been established and the key technical problems identified, one can plan experiments; from these experiments one can plan the design and manufacture of test equipment, and so on. Planning development work to this extent cannot be as precise in time and cost as the planning of a production program — and the plans must be subject to change — but proceeding on a development program without a plan, schedule, and estimate of cost usually turns out to be a costly and time-consuming process.

There is also the consideration that men frequently are creative under pressure — and continual pressure to meet a schedule is good.

Let me remind you that these comments pertain to development work and not to research — basic or applied.

Q. Do not most businesses have a research department?

A. Companies in the technical field generally maintain a *development* organization but not many support what can properly be called *research.* Inflation of terms has caused drafting to be called design, and design to be called development, and development to be called research — to the confusion of everyone. What most companies urgently need is a good engineering design organization. A limited number can afford advanced development work on their own. Very few can justify research, in these days when the *research* programs of the largest industrial organizations are a tiny fraction of the national total research expenditure.

Q. Technological results have to be sold. Additional capital is needed do develop ideas. What about examining the value of investment or expected return on research? One product may show a substantial payoff; another none. This leads to the need for experimental research, doesn't it?

A. Again there is a semantic problem. When a product can be identified as the outcome of experimentation, I would refer to the process as development and not research. Development work intended to yield new products should be guided by forecasts of sales and profits which assume that the reasonably optimistic forecasts of performance will be realized. Experimentation on the key technical problems refines the knowledge of physical performance and permits improvement in the forecast of the market; and so forth. No matter how murky the view ahead may be, it is worth the effort to project costs out to the production stage still early in the development cycle; and to correct it as new data becomes available.

One thing to remember is that busy operating organizations, including their integral engineering and laboratory groups, almost never develop radically new products. Current problems cause such pressure that long-range development is usually disregarded by them — until they run out of products, as sometimes occurs. New products can be expected only from organizations dedicated to this end.

Q. Who, then, will do basic research and finance it?

A. There is little basic research now being conducted in industry. There are a few large companies which have supported truly basic research in fields related to their business; other basic research is found in industry but limited in scope and direction. However, in the aggregate this work is small as compared to the basic research of the universities, the research institutes, and the government laboratories. Whether this situation is desirable or not, it is the practical result of the combined effect of uncertainty over research results, competitive pressures within industry, and the availability of government funds for these research institutions. Under existing financial and political conditions, I am convinced that industry is unwise to spend its own funds for basic research. Industrial efforts should concentrate on applying the results of research to new developments and to the related applied research.

Who then should do the research and how should it be financed? Government support of basic research is not deeply imbedded in our system and I think industry should base its plans on this fact. Furthermore, the funds for basic work are available only to non-profit organizations — or substantially so. It will become increasingly important for industry to influence the distribution of these funds so as to support a steady advance in all branches of industry.

In making these remarks, I was concerned not with what the situation ought to be, but rather with what it really is.

Q. Did you say that we should push men through the development activity and into production work?

A. Yes, and for several reasons. In the first place, development work is probably the most demanding and unrewarding phase of technical industry; few men are competent and even fewer remain so over a long period. There are exceptions but in general it is suited to young men, and "graduation" to other technical work such as engineering, manufacturing, or marketing should be normal.

Another consideration is that the development and production of truly novel products usually brings in some problems in technical sales, in manufacture, in product service. At the outset at least, only developmental groups are qualified to handle these problems. It is effective to move the men or some of them at least along with the product to avoid discontinuities between functions.

A third consideration is that decisions made in the development work tend to make commitments which affect manufacturing and marketing. Some individuals in the development group should have had experience in these areas, and this end can be accomplished by allowing some to follow the product through — and then return to development.

Q. What is your distinction between research and development? The need for probing into new principles?

A. Development work is aimed at specific objectives, beyond the state of the art, at results that you can use commercially or militarily.

Q. Aspects of research, then, must be more focused toward the commercial end point?

A. The confusion between research and development is more than a semantic question; it is producing a real effect in the inefficient management of the national research and development programs, and is resulting in costs which are greater than necessary for the same end results.

Q. We need better selection of development objectives.

A. The chance of a hit is very low if you just explore in general. Conversion of research results into useful hardware is an important activity — as important to the nation as research. We need to place more emphasis on the work of the engineer.

Q. Is it possible and better to change your project leaders before a project gets into trouble?

A. That's what I hope we can be smart enough to do.

Q. Real research is something for other companies? I think there's some inconsistency in your position. You're saying that we should go around searching in various laboratories and the various universities. And, as I recall from college, you won't even get in the front door unless you were doing research on your own because research people just won't bother to spend the time of day with you.

A. I didn't give the whole paper in my talk. I said you had to have a "ticket of admission." You must have some people on advanced work *all* the time.

Q. Right, but what I'm saying is that if you summed up all the tickets of admission, if everybody simultaneously made the decision they weren't going to do research — I think this country would be in sorry shape. I think this country's going to be in sorry shape unless it gives real attention to the research end of things.

A. This possibility does not frighten me because I do not regard much of what is now done in industry as research. Most of what is called research is really development work aimed at rather specific objectives. When I say this, I do not mean to depreciate what industry is doing, but only to point out that it is not properly called research.

It is my impression that there would be available to industry an adequate number of scientists to maintain contact with basic research — if industry recruited, either as consultants or on a full-time basis, scientists who have passed the stage of active research. Many companies have done so. However, you may be right in believing that in the long run some basic research in-house may be necessary to maintain this "ticket of admission."

Q. I think that generally it's been agreed that our reduction in costs for various kinds of things over a period of time in terms of real dollars or real earning power is primarily due to technological change and not merely new process control or other devices of that sort. Do you agree?

A. Yes, if you add the substitution of new materials.

Q. I'm concerned about a couple of things. First, the remarks made this morning to the point that results that come out of research have to be sold because additional capital is needed to develop them. Second, the fact that research isn't desirable in most companies. To my mind, the fact that we can abrogate our responsibility to cooperate or estimate the value of the results by hiding behind a budget must be forestalled. I'd like to offer a suggestion to help this come into being, namely, that we put more burden of responsibility on the engineering people and the marketing people in the upper division. We should think well ahead in the context of studies such as the first speaker this morning, Dr. Raymond, mentioned. To be more specific than that, what energy do we save? Not what assembly of black boxes do we play with? And if we have research results with these certain characteristics, the idea comes to a business review. Then turn these over to the marketing people and the production people to assess the value of the problem if solved. By looking at our research in its more fundamental aspects and quantitatively relating it to product possibilities one project might show substantial payoff. Only two or three great technological developments are needed, if successful. I think we can place a dollar value of prospective return on the problem, and thus get a differential consideration of the value of research without your people saying where research will pay off. Thus, we may see some research as possibly paying off in several areas. Almost certainly it will hit in some one of these areas.

A. We certainly have a semantic problem here, because one cannot think about what I call research in this fashion. Research seeks an end which is not known; that's why it's research. If we used your ideas and said "development," then perhaps it might work. But I'm convinced that no operating organization, through its main chain of command, will ever come up with *radically* new products.

Q. You mean that existing organizations are normally too set on their problems to know what they're talking about?

A. If you talk to them about future new products when business is good, they are busy getting their product out the door and they don't want to bother with you. And when business is slow, you can't sell them a development project. My thesis is that any company in the technical field ought to have at least a minimum staff thinking ahead, and defining long-range goals and evaluating these goals in the light of scientific discoveries. But if you put a dollar value on the problems which the operating divisions define as the one they'd like to get solved, you won't get any questions about scientific progress because it isn't their problem, *yet*.

Operating divisions are busy with the product. If you ask them what they want, they'll polish their antiques to the nth degree. That's all they can see. "I'm having trouble with this part now and I want something that'll last twice as long!" That's their argument, in essence. Well, they ought to do that work themselves. *Anything they can define for themselves, they ought to do for themselves in their own engineering group.*

I've spent fifteen years on this kind of work. If you want to develop new products, dedicate some people to this end. If they don't develop new products, they don't eat. When this work is in an operating division, they will say, "We were so busy putting out fires we didn't have time to go think about new products." I could name some men in pretty big research laboratories whose directors have told me, "We spend three-quarters of our time putting out fires." And these are supposed to be research groups! Now if they are mixed in with the operating people, the pressure of the day-to-day product line is severe: "We're having trouble and the first team has got to get out there. Drop your long-range stuff and get this fixed now!" — That's what happens and logically so. Novel products are not likely under such circumstances.

Q. Couldn't they at least be asked or challenged to define the long-range company needs so that they can reflect against themselves?

Q. If we accept your definition of research, if we agree that the manufacturing divisions are not to engage in it, who is going to do it? Who is going to pay for research for basic facts and principles?

A. Industries should support some of it. But the major share of research is being done by universities and independent engineering schools and through research establishments like Batelle, A. D. Little, and Stanford Research Institute. It's being done well there and the volume is growing. If you add the research of all nations together, there's a tremendous store of knowledge of basic physical relationships and it is growing. It's hard to keep track of what's being done. So you need people who are knowledgeable and understand these results. Maybe you could have more such people by supporting a research lab.

Q. I'm asking who is going to pay for it. You say we must sponsor this research more and more through government channels.

A. I don't say that's the only way to do it. I don't say a company which can afford it shouldn't; some should and do. However, if I were responsible for spending the money of a company with, say, two hundred million dollars in sales and corresponding profits, I don't think I would let myself be talked into basic research. The chance is too small that the results would be beneficial *to that* business.

Q. Several times you've alluded to the possibility of pushing research men through the development activity in order to get effective management of new projects.

A. Oh, yes, Mr. Smith talked about that. I think practically all engineers ought to come in through the development organization.

Q. You've come to this several times. I was wondering if you'd like to discuss it just a little bit more because it's a pretty serious change of concept for some of us.

A. Transfer of the technical information *with the people* when the projects moves from laboratory to production is the key argument. If you feel you've got a package ready for development, you'd better transfer the key people. Otherwise, you will run into a barrier; and the next group will say, "Well, we didn't invent this. We've got to review the whole situation. Our reputation is at stake." So you lose time and waste money.

Q. Among creative scientists there is the possibility, of course, of starting many arguments that way. Who gets to move? Who gets to stay? These things aren't just accepted!

A. In basic research laboratories, there are some men who should stay there permanently. But most of the industrial labs are engaged in development work. The men I am thinking of are in that part of the business and ought to go on with the product. Someday they should be managers of an operating unit.

Q. You're making generalizations about overhead that are spottily true. By making them general, you make it sound as though everybody's doing the same thing. We, and a lot of other companies, are doing very comprehensive audits of what we call management costs. Some people question whether we aren't doing more than we should on fairly undefinable jobs. I think if maybe you phrased this that some people ought to take a good look at their overhead costs . . . For example, I don't know the figure for enginering development. It's hard to say, but there're probably at least an equal number of companies that do get the overhead strictly under control. I know that I do. We know our overhead meticulously and what it can do. In fact, we do this for the very reasons that you're talking about.

In engineering organizations I think that research contracting under government sponsorship has caused us to make these activities very inefficient and unproductive. And today there's increased ability to maintain our organization by putting in better communications and providing more service to the greater number of engineers. You can get more out of it for less dollars. I'm with you 100% on this need for financial measurement in technical things.

A. (Dr. Raymond) I call it "stupid arithmetic." But it happens to be very worthwhile to go through this stupid arithmetic in any situation. Too many R & D and management people don't even go through elementary economics of their projects. They never ask, "What'll happen if this is good?" They get so intrigued with the fact that this is a new technical possibility that they never realize that it may not be worth an economic damn.

Q. My question basically is whether or not you can make these very refined distinctions between research and development. I think that, probably, successful development calls for some probing around for new principles. This probing into development cost will deteriorate into excess paperwork very rapidly. I wonder if you wouldn't agree?

A. Oh, I agree with you. I've gone through things pretty fast. What I'm saying is that development work is aimed at specific objectives. The development man gets his data and goes on. The research man gets intrigued with the subject and wants to round it out and write a paper on this general phenomena. That, of course, is a good thing if you're a scientist; but for the development project it's financial murder.

Q. What you're essentially saying is that the objectives of the research simply must become more focused as they move toward the commercial end point.

A. I said the development must become more focused. I really think semantics creates a problem. I have worked with a company in California for about three years now. First I helped them with their engineering organization. They are a big company, and due to their basic interest they felt they should do research. They set up a research laboratory and they told the lab people, "You are the Research Department." The Research Department said, "Well, we can try, but what shall we do?" It was a problem. Soon we had to get an operating manager of experience and reputation to take charge of this "research" for about a year and a half. He made them realize that they were not doing research; that they were in the development business; and that their objectives should be such as to yield a profit.

Q. If you look at the men coming out of graduate school with physics, and particularly in the electrical engineering segment, etc., the very best men wouldn't take the job in the kind of area you just described. Now, I want to know how you're going to get them?

A. Well, I don't know how you're going to get them, but I think we're hurting bad for the shortage of them. It is my feeling that the whole development program (and I mean development) in this country is costing at least twice what it should because of this shortage.

Q. I think it's the other way around. I think if we'd spend the money on examining the development end, we'd do a better job of selection before we started off on half of these projects. That's where we'd save money, not in the basic research end. We should open basic research real wide, then do a very careful job of selection at the development end — which is the expensive end, as you pointed out.

A. True; but you represent a pretty big company and can exploit most of what you find. But for many companies — and I'm thinking about the whole range of companies needing new products — many companies are participating in the whole area of research. The chance of hitting with basic research in their own area is like setting a pencil on the end and expecting it to fall at the 360-degree mark. If they explore in general, the chance of hitting something in their own field is terribly poor.

Q. I don't know about exploring in general, but I bet their chances of success are a lot better if they'd spend a little more of their investment on the research end that you're talking about, including digging way back to the roots and picking the one that makes the best sense, instead of just picking one at random.

A. You're going to make me go read my whole paper.

Q. Have you been saying that we've had too much talk about science and scientists, and too much glamor about research, and not enough emphasis on making things happen in the production end?

Q. I really don't think we're giving too much emphasis to research. But we are not giving enough emphasis to the technique of converting research results and resulting design concepts into hardware which is usable. And that's a very difficult problem. Development is the most difficult occupation I know of. You get little credit because much of the results "leak" out into the operating departments. If things go well some other manager replaces you because you got fouled up on production or something, and he comes along and gets the firm out of difficulties. In research you can go in many directions at once and this floundering isn't noticed. That's the way it should be. Development is aimed, and must produce results. So I don't want to give the impression I'm against development. I just want more attention to translating ideas into producible products.

IDENTIFYING AND EVALUATING THE
BARRIER PROBLEMS IN TECHNOLOGY

WARD C. LOW

WARD C. LOW

Member, Advanced Planning Staff
MITRE Corporation
Bedford, Massachusetts

Dr. Low received his B.S. in Physics from the University of Wyoming and his Ph.D. in Physics from Boston University. From 1948 to 1954 he served in various capacities in Boston University's Upper Atmosphere Research Laboratory. After spending a year at Massachusetts Institute of Technology, he joined the Sylvania Missile Systems Laboratory as manager of the Aero-Physics Department. From 1958 to 1960 he was a staff member, Ballistic Missile Defense Branch, Advanced Research Projects Agency, The Pentagon, Washington, D.C. Here he participated in major studies appraising the technological potential of new fields as applied to military requirements and developments. In 1961 he became a Staff Specialist, Development Planning, Sylvania Electronics Systems Division. Late in 1961 he moved to his present position. His professional interest has centered around a rigorous analysis of technological opportunities and barriers as presented by scientific progress and technological needs.

Identifying and Evaluating the
Barrier Problems in Technology

Before we become involved extensively with the problem, let us inquire as to why the job referred to in the title should be done, from the point of view of the planner in technology. The title suggests that barrier problems in technology exist, and further, that such problems can be identified and evaluated. "Technology" is usually considered to be *applied* science and engineering, as contrasted with "pure science." Now, we would all agree that certain hypothetical innovations can be isolated which are not demonstrably at variance with the accepted laws of pure science. But the accomplishment of such innovations may be very difficult to support immediately with realizable engineering specifications. The principal engineering difficulties that can be seen to stand in the way are here referred to as "barriers." It may seem strange that we should concern ourselves with hypothetical achievements, but this must be the case as the planner looks ahead at future developments in technology.

Direct observation shows that the status levels of corporations, military groups, and even nations rise or fall on the leading edge of advancing technology. Therefore, it is of vital importance to be concerned with that leading edge; this is the domain in which the technological planner must operate. The problem is complicated by the fact that many innovations which may be hypothesized, even those that are not clearly at variance with physical principles, will turn out to be of no direct importance to us. Hence, a process is required for evaluating the probable levels of importance which may attach to the overcoming of various classes of barriers. The successful long-range planner will identify and properly evaluate those barrier problems whose modification or solution may be of importance to his home organization. Our attention will be specifically directed toward this subject in the present discussion.

NOTE: Some of the ideas developed herein were exercised while the author was senior staff specialist (Development Planning) at Sylvania Electronic Systems, Waltham, Massachusetts.

The objectives of this paper are (a) to underscore the high significance of technological innovation; (b) to examine some of the main features of technological barriers; (c) to outline an approach to the problem of identification and evaluation of significant barriers; and (d) to illustrate some of the results of such an approach.

Although there may appear herein an emphasis on problems related to the military, I trust this will not immediately limit the reader's interest. Much, if not all, of what follows seems also to have equal applicability to nonmilitary technology.

Some Technological Barriers of the Past and Present

Let us try to develop some means of sensing whence values arise in some technological developments with which we are already somewhat familiar.

For example, consider submarines for a moment. A submarine is a vehicle which is capable of carrying man from place to place when submerged in a fluid medium. The fact that the liquid medium (water) is very plentiful on the earth's surface, and that its properties are markedly different from the solid-gaseous interface in which man is otherwise required to move, renders the achievement of such an engineering capability of considerable importance.

On the other hand, achievement of capability for powered flight in air involves not only a new medium,[1] but also in an important way a new *dimension* (the vertical).[2] Note, in the case of aircraft, that the negotiable magnitude in the new dimension is small in comparison to the pertinent standard — the radius of the earth. In fact, the dimensions in which aircraft operation is of the order of an earth-radius lie parallel to the earth's surface, the dimensions in which man has been constrained to move until now. But the maximum velocity of travel was increased in aircraft by an order of magnitude (from tens of miles per hour to hundreds).

In comparison with aircraft, orbital space-flight permits hori-

[1] Note also that the air-medium is isotropic on a world-wide scale, whereas other media (water, land) have boundaries which restrict horizontal motion.

[2] Of course, the submarine also performs in the vertical dimension to some extent, but this aspect by itself seems to be relatively unimportant, compared to the strong effects due to the water medium.

zontal movements which are *large* in total mileage, as compared to an earth-radius; at the same time, the associated velocity has risen another two orders of magnitude (from hundreds of miles per hour to tens of thousands). But, in terms of degree of achievement (and likely results therefrom), successful space-flight *beyond* earth-orbit may outweigh the significance of aircraft or earth-orbital bodies. For it is in the case of deep-space flight that man first attains a "fully" three-dimensional capability. ("Fully" must still be qualified, in the sense that man still cannot penetrate freely and at will into solid media, such as the earth presents; hence his travel is sharply curtailed in the vertical direction *downward*, below the surface of the solid earth.)

Large leaps in man's capabilities can occur in dimensions which are not spatial in character. Take the energy dimension, for example. Here, too, tremendous steps have recently been taken, in connection with nuclear fusion and nuclear fission. Just doubling the power of explosives and fuels would have been a notable achievement, but nuclear fusion has multiplied the available power concentrations by more than a million.

As another example of violent increase in certain aspects of capability, consider today's high-speed digital computers. Their speed of operation is now on the order of 100,000 times faster than a human's, and the machine produces far fewer errors per million computations. This large percentage improvement over man's unaided capacities certainly represents the breaching of very important technological barriers. We will consider later some of the future promise in the area of machine computation.

It is worth noting that, in the preceding discussions, it was not necessary to bring out *in detail* what the new capabilities were "good for." We can be quite confident that large changes in *fundamental* physical characteristics — volume, mass, velocity, energy density, dimensional capacities, etc. — carry with them a corresponding change in potential level of human interest.

Categories of Technology

It appears that all aspects of technology can be classified broadly in one or another of the following three categories: (a) signal handling, (b) energy conversion, and (c) materials processing. There are also other categories which may be particularly helpful under special circumstances. The point that can be made here is twofold. First, that a small number of reasonably homogeneous classes exist which can be essentially complete from a morphological point of view. And, second, that appropriate classification can bring forward the results of otherwise unrelated cumulative studies, which apply to equipment properties of the selected classes. For example, suppose that wide-ranging studies in the area of signal handling tended to show that major developments are very likely to occur in the field of self-organizing systems (i.e., adaptive, perceptive, learning, or intelligent machines). Then such analyses can be taken over at once and adapted to the special conditions which may be suitable to any particular problem that we may classify as part of signal-handling technology.

Even in the event that suitable broad-scale studies are not already available, appropriate classification is of paramount importance, in terms of basic scientific understanding. This is inevitable, since the latter understanding rests in a fundamental way upon the drawing of similes and contrasts between a new item and other related ones which may be more familiar. It usually happens that more than one type of classification is possible for a given item. Useful understanding often results from exploring the different relationships which are suggested by different types of classification.

Further Characteristics of Important
Technological Innovations

Thus far, we have looked at some generalized properties of some important examples of technological innovations, and we have emphasized the importance of suitable classifications of technological ideas. We now look more closely into the properties of innovations.

One observation is that precursors, or roots, of innovations extend into the past in a recognizable form. The key ideas are generally available well in advance of the actual introduction of an innovation — they are just lost in the "noise." Each of us, I am sure, has had the experience of being shown a novel idea, with the mental reaction: "I thought along similar lines some time ago." The reason we did not give proper evaluation to the idea's promise (assuming it was within our area of principal activity where we should have done so) is often that we just failed to recognize the special significance thereof, as it lay among many other ideas which competed for our main attention.

What can help us to recognize promising ideas more effectively in our principal field of interest? A very helpful aid can be found in answering the question: What classes of hypothetical innovations, which could relate to my field of interest, carry high promise of widespread application and/or sizable advance in some basic capability? In some cases, one can exhibit high-value applicability of a class of hypothetical innovations. To that extent, the innovation tends to reflect the needs found in common experience. On the other hand, clear-cut demands for potential advances of a fundamental nature are often more difficult to demonstrate, since basic advances tend to introduce new kinds of capabilities with which we have had little or no experience. Thus, a revolutionary mode of preserving food might be readily evaluated, since we are accustomed to various other modes of doing the same thing. However, the value of space-flight capabilities (adding a full third dimension to man's travel capabilities) is still in doubt in some quarters, mainly because we have never had such capabilities in the past, and we have few, if any, built-in requirements for them. A similar experience developed in connection with powered air flight — initial reaction in many quarters was one of doubt as to useful applicability. But it seems very probable that, in both airborne and space flight, the significant increases in dimensional capabilities are by themselves enough to guarantee an immense eventual impact upon humanity. In other words, truly basic advances will find important applications eventually, even though it may be difficult to visualize such values at any given time. For example, it may now be hard to see features of general engineering importance which result from the recognition by Yang and Lee of the failure of parity in weak interactions. Yet it may very well be that eventually such will appear.

Other characteristic features of technological innovations are worth noting. In particular, their engineering effect is always to render difficult or impractical tasks easier (or sometimes unnecessary). Thus, for purposes of barrier-identification, we can afford to assume the successful solution of any *engineering* problem (while remaining within basic physical boundaries), since this is the actual direction in which future developments will carry us. Indeed, as indicated earlier, innovations will usually turn out to be important in an engineering sense to the extent that they actually permit breaching of significant barriers. Therefore it seems logical to give attention to determining the general characteristics of technological barriers in selected areas of interest, since this should lead to a capability for estimating means and values of overcoming them.

Identification and Evaluation of Barriers

As we have already suggested, important barriers tend to be associated with accomplishments which would exhibit (a) widespread applicability, and/or (b) a large extension of some fundamental capability. Thus, in space flight one would like to have large and cheap booster capability; adaptable control devices which are capable of effective learning in a new environment would also be of interest, among other things. The corresponding barriers are describable in terms of those prime engineering variables which determine fundamental performance in the given area. For example, in the narrow case of space-propulsion, we could identify one class of barriers as those which make it difficult to achieve high specific impulse simultaneously with large thrust-to-weight ratio. In the case of intelligent or learning machines, in a real sense the identification of specific barriers is a part of the principal problem, since much of what may contribute to intelligence on the part of machines (or on the part of humans, for that matter) is not clearly specifiable. However, microelectronic techniques can be seen clearly to represent one class of important barrier in this case, since no matter what the details of structure, a great many similar units ("neurons") will be needed in a small space. Fortunately, most areas of interest are not quite so diffuse. For cases in which barriers can be specified, we can outline some steps whereby the task of specific evaluation of barriers may be approached.

In terms of operational steps that can be taken to advantage, one may suggest the following illustrative sequence.

First, specify as clearly as possible the basic technological objectives which are of prime interest, initially broadly and then more particularly as may be appropriate. In the very particular and simplified case of space flight, it may be desired economically to place large loads of instrumentation, equipment, and people into controllable orbits around the earth and in trajectories which will permit physical exploration of the planets of our solar system, permitting the return of selected instruments and men to earth for safe recovery.

Second, examine the goals which are implied by the basic technological objectives in terms of their related areas and classes of technology. The propulsion goal which is connected with space flight can be thought of to advantage in connection with related problems of energy conversion. This at once brings to mind a variety of means whereby energy can be converted from one form to another, including chemical, nuclear, electrostatic, electromagnetic, gravitational, and other interactions. Basic physical limits and characteristics of such major subclassifications are more or less known and available. These should be specified on a common basis as clearly as possible for purposes of intercomparison. Multiple cuts at this problem from different points of view are highly desirable in order to achieve a stable set of conclusions.[3]

Third, while staying within recognizable physical limits, seriously and imaginatively survey in the above contexts all possibly interesting results which might be achieved if various specified engineering problems were solved. This has already been done in some respects for the above example of rocket propulsion, in the sense that theoretical limits of propulsive efficiency for a variety of substances and modes of propulsion have already been calculated.

Fourth, rank the hypothetical capabilities (as studied in the third step above) in order by value, in terms of their potential contribution to achievement of the specified goals, taking also into account the "fallout" benefits which might accrue to other desirable goals. Thus, a nuclear source of space-propulsion promises a unique combination of high specific impulse and high thrust-weight ratio, and might therefore be accorded high value, as compared to chemical propellants; further, developments in

---

[3] Long-range plans run the risk of completely missing the point that eventually turns out to be important, due to changes in the basic nature of the significant questions. Requirements which appear to be in heavy demand from a variety of different points of view will tend to hold their validity over a longer period.

nuclear propulsion could have direct effects on nonspace propulsion and power production.

Fifth, outline the principal technological steps which would be required in order to reach those capabilities which have been rated as having high value. If truly advanced capability is hypothesized, there will often be serious gaps in the sequence of specifiable steps. Indeed, in some cases it will appear that one does not have any clear idea at all of how he might undertake to achieve certain specifiable capabilities having high value. In other cases, the required steps may be such as to permit clear delineation thereof. In the example of propulsion listed above, hypothetical photon propulsion systems involve rather more gaps in their engineering specifications than does ion propulsion.

Sixth, select a small number of high-value capabilities which have "reasonably" well-specifiable steps for further examination and possible recommendation for full-scale study and research and development. One should at this point once again review the matter of class homogeneity, scope, and coverage, in order to insure a balanced set of R & D recommendations. At this juncture in our example, one might select a number of key elements for R & D in nuclear and ionic propulsion, while starting no serious work now on photon propulsion.

Seventh, remain alert for those developments which could conceivably and significantly modify the value ratings, or could fill in grossly missing steps toward achieving capabilities having high value.

Further Developments in the Area of Data Processing (Signal Handling)

In addition to the rudimentary examples related to rocket propulsion given above, we can mention the results of a planning study which has been done using an approach like that outlined here. In this case, the goals were specified for study purposes to be the development and maintenance of technical leadership in data processing capabilities over the next twenty years. As the study progressed, it appeared repeatedly, from almost whatever starting point was taken, that hypothetical developments of greatest interest would be those which are closely associated in one way or another with development of self-organizing capabilities, with all that a very general interpretation of that term implies. We noted earlier that the complete identification of specific technological barriers is quite muddy in the case of self-organizing systems; even so, the general result of the study was unequivocal in leading to the expectation of very great advances in areas associated with self-organizing systems. It should be noted that clear *physical* limits are very hard to find in this case, which underscores the probability of large and rapid progress being made.

Conclusion

We have pointed out some of the reasons which lead one to focus attention upon the barrier problems in technology, since it is in the solution of some of those problems that we will find the developing bases for new technologies. The suggestion has been made that one can profitably evaluate the several barriers that are of potential interest by assuming they have been overcome, and by estimating (under various conditions) the probable values which can be associated with the capabilities which could result. Estimates of difficulties in overcoming the associated engineering barriers, together with the value estimates of such achievements, can provide an effective base for planning and justifying advanced research and development.

Q. You pointed out the need of choosing "high value" technical alternatives, particularly with respect to military developments. How do you do this?

A. This is a key question, and of course a principal difficulty. One must identify effective and stable goals. If you cannot find a goal-directed basis for clearcut preference among several technical alternatives, you may wish to go further down several of the possible paths before a final selection is made. Where other criteria do not provide firm guidance, one picks that alternative which is least sensitive to major uncertainties, and at the same time provides major advances in basic capabilities.

Q. What techniques would you suggest for better identifying today's activities which will constitute tomorrow's advances of technological innovations?

A. Actually, my paper was addressed to this question. I will just go back over some high points again. First, what are you basically trying to accomplish technologically — what are your goals? What principal elements of technology bear upon your problems? What large changes in these elements would affect your business? What classes of new technology could markedly affect your present goals or modes of operation? Certain types of technological advances seem repeatedly to come up when such questions are asked. In military electronics, such advances are illustrated by micro-electronic techniques, and by self-organizing systems, as we mentioned earlier.

[At this point Dr. Low asked the audience to suggest an industry against which he would demonstrate the kind of technical examination he had proposed. "Railroads" was offered, and Dr. Low raised a series of questions about their fundamental technological limitations. Some discussion follows.]

Q. You mentioned the railroads, Dr. Low. I was thinking now that our railroads are trying desperately to become two-dimensional and three-dimensional. We've been essentially one-dimensional transportation.

A. One of the ways that you can become two-dimensional is by carrying trucks on your flatbed cars. Do you have some other ideas like this?

Q. We've never found a technology that can overcome political obsolescence.

A. What would have happened if this kind of thinking about transportation had been tried earlier by the railroads? Would you still get frozen in politically?

Q. Well, the Boston & Maine, for example, started Northeast Airlines and the Government legislated them out of it.

A. I was thinking of the trucking lines.

Q. We were legislated out of the trucking lines in 1935. We could not go beyond our own railroad. In addition, we could not serve the key points out of the railroad since 1935. The Boston & Maine then carried traffic between Boston and Fitchburg by truck.

A. Is there any exclusion on ground effect machines? Are you frozen out of them too? Are you excluded from using conveyor belts?

Q. No, but we don't have the right of eminent domain. That's an important barrier in itself, and it's easier to visualize some of these things. Railroads do run pipelines and we're not legislated out of that.

Q. (Raymond) I'd like to comment on your statement on value. You said that you cannot assign arbitrary and absolute values to any one of these things we're talking about. But you can certainly get comparative values and use them with a small amount of exercise of the imagination. By the process, say, of establishing a task and comparing various ways of doing this task, in addition to what it costs you to do it in the first place.

A. To the extent that you can estimate costs, I agree that this is the common denominator.

Q. I think cost is fundamental when it comes up time and time again, as in the technical-economical analysis that Dean O'Brien was talking about. I happen to share a joke with many about operations research in general: It's the process by which you take bad data and put them through a doubtful mathematical model and come up with results that defy common sense. But, in fact, you can get very good guidelines.

A. And I certainly agree that you only get relative measures in many cases — but often that's enough.

Q. Dr. Raymond, I think your point is that this figure of merit you're after is a 100% kind of comparison. If you're down within 10% or 15%, it's often good enough for a decision.

A. We've had the occasion, for example, of laying out a task, then writing out on paper ten different ways of accomplishing this. We then find ourselves coming up with a factor of 10 between them. That's the guide to indicate how we ought to go.

Q. What I meant was the basic fundamental criteria for your problems. You talk about the anti-ICBM problem, for example. You can look at various systems like Nike, Zeus, Plato, etc., and say, "This one is cheapest." But then you run into the basic question: Shall we try to shoot down ICBMs? This is getting into really tough problems.

A. Oh, I really don't think so. I think you can find better ways to look at these problems and here I've presented one of them.

NATURAL RESOURCES PROJECTIONS AND THEIR CONTRIBUTION TO TECHNOLOGICAL PLANNING

JOSEPH L. FISHER
HANS H. LANDSBERG

JOSEPH L. FISHER

President
Resources For The Future, inc.
Washington, D.C.

From 1947 through 1953 Dr. Fisher served as an economist and administrative assistant to the Chairman in the Council of Economic Advisers, Executive Office of the President. Before World War II he worked with the National Resources Planning Board and taught at several universities. In 1954 and 1955 he served as staff director of the President's Cabinet Committee on Energy Supplies and Resources Policy. Since 1954 he has been associated with the management of Resources For The Future, inc., a nonprofit research and educational foundation concerned with the development of natural resources. He received his Ph.D. in Economics from Harvard University in 1947.

HANS H. LANDSBERG

Director, Resource Appraisal Program
Resources For The Future, inc.
Washington, D.C.

*Mr. Landsberg was born in Germany. He received his B.Sc. (Econ.) degree from the London School of Economics in 1936 and his M.A. from Columbia University in 1941. From 1939 to 1942 he was with the National Bureau of Economic Research and co-authored with Harold Barger the Bureau's Output Employ-*ment, and Productivity in American Agriculture, 1899-1939. *Following service with the Office of Strategic Services in Washington and the Mediterranean Theater of Operations from 1942 to 1945 he was in private business as a consulting economist. He joined the staff of Resources For the Future, inc., in 1960.*

Natural Resources Projections and Their Contribution to Technological Planning

Technological planning — that is, planning for the creation, development, and adoption in industry of new and improved technology — lies near the heart of economic growth for the individual firm and for the whole country. This kind of planning both within firms and in certain public agencies has spread rapidly in recent years. A number of private firms and government agencies have notable long-range planning programs. Among these may be mentioned public (investor-owned, government-regulated) utilities, major steel companies, airlines, federal government construction agencies, and larger municipalities. Public electric power utilities and gas pipeline companies examine market possibilities 20 or more years ahead and schedule the construction of new capacity and the introduction of new technology. Federal construction agencies such as the Corps of Engineers maintain six-year advance programs of construction projects; more general planning for rivers and harbors work and for other purposes extends much farther into the future.

For the most part advance planning, private or public, pertains to the opportunities and problems of particular organizations and the products or services they deal in. Frequently the specific plans are not put in the larger context of the industry, geographic region, or national and world market *in a systematic and disciplined way*. We are aware that the trend is definitely toward the preparation of more comprehensive technical and economic information relating to the future, but much more could usefully be done.[1]

A distinction needs to be drawn here between what we call natural resource projections and technological planning. By

[1] National Planning Association, *Uses of Long-Range Economic Projections: Some Survey Findings,* Technical Supplement No. 5, National Projection Series, Washington, D.C., August 1960. Almost 90% of the respondents in this survey, chiefly larger enterprises, reported that they used long-range projections of the general economy in their planning. But the major portion of the business community probably does not make use of such projections, according to the survey.

natural resource projections we mean disciplined, systematic forward estimates of demand for and supply of land in its various uses — crop and grazing land, urban land, recreation sites, forest land; water, energy commodities, and metallic and nonmetallic minerals — both individual items and general categories. Demand and supply estimates for the various items are interrelated to take account of substitutions among them, and are consistent with projections of the broad capability of the economy in terms of its labor force, investment rates, productivity, foreign trade, and the like.

By technological planning we mean, as noted previously, the rational taking account of all factors relevant to the creation, development, and adoption in industry of new and improved techniques, products, or services. The process of technological planning may be subdivided as follows:

1. Identification of problems and opportunities (preliminary technological and economic appraisal).
2. Research.
3. Development (pilot operations with materials and cost records kept).
4. Definitive economic appraisal (costs, markets, pricing, economies of scale and joint production, competition).
5. Scheduling and budgeting of the innovation.
6. Actual adoption in industry (organizing the capital, labor, raw materials, etc., to do the job).
7. Periodic evaluation.
8. Ideas for further technological planning.

Throughout there will be a concern for education and training of personnel for all phases of the process of technological planning.

The focus of our paper will be on natural resources projections, as these are derived from and adjusted to more aggregative demographic, technologic, and economic projections. The general methodology for making natural resources projections will be explained briefly and a few specific projections for 1980 and 2000 will be presented. These are drawn from a study which carries the provisional title, *Resources in America's Future,* now nearing completion in Resources For The Future. A number of possible resource shortages which come clearly into view in this systematic looking ahead will then be considered in more detail. These problems represent challenges and opportunities for technological planning. The last part of the paper will suggest in several major resource fields a number of newer technological prospects which are already, or soon may be, important subjects for technological planning.

The most significant point the paper will try to make is that technological planning for specific purposes in particular firms and agencies can be done more effectively against a backdrop of systematic, long-term projections of the demand for and supply of natural resources. These projections can furnish a useful framing or perspective for the technological planning of the particular firms and agencies. This will be especially true for firms which develop basic resources or process raw materials, plus those firms closely connected with such activities, and firms that are in the business of creating substitutes, such as various branches of the chemical industry.

Natural Resource Projections for the Years 1980 and 2000

The basic inputs for the economy, as well as for individual firms, are labor and enterprise, capital, and resources including raw materials. All are necessary, although within limits one may be substituted for another. Estimated demand for any one of these, or for any sub-item, must be accommodated within projections of the over-all capacity and performance of the economy. Further, there must be internal consistency among the amounts, spatial and industrial distribution, and scheduling of use of the various components. On the supply side requirements will have to be met out of the existing and potential number of people, their skills, the supply of savings and investment funds for capital formation and replacement, and the amounts, distribution, and potentialities for resource and raw materials. Technology and economics form the bridge between estimated demands and the levels and manner in which they are satisfied. With advanced, promptly adopted technology, requirements can be filled more quickly and efficiently. With the skillful balancing of the variety of supply possibilities with estimated demands, with careful attention to the estimating of net returns of alternative courses of action and to the economies of scale, the development of the economy can proceed along the economic lines.

Projections of demand for and supply of resource and raw materials can form one important basis for technological planning and economic adoption in industry. The following table presents estimates for 1980 and 2000 of the demand for a number of important resource and raw materials. Projections are also presented of population, labor force, gross national product, and investment. These may be thought of as a portrayal of the likely capability of the economy for 20 and 40 years ahead. Within these aggregative projections, and consistent with them, the demands for the more specific materials have been worked out. The economy has been divided into three parts along its vertical dimension; major end-use categories, such as food, shelter, transportation, heat and power, and the like; intermediate materials which have been carried some distance in processing from the basic resources but are still not highly specific in use, such as lumber, steel, and aluminum; and the more basic resources and raw materials, such as land in its several major uses, water, and relatively unprocessed minerals and fuels. The diagram on page 124 (Figure 1) illustrates our estimating system in such a way that some of the interrelations may be visualized.

In the larger study from which these estimates have been drawn, demands for specific materials, as well as the more aggregative items, are presented in ranges: high, low, and medium. The medium projections are presented here, although for many analytical purposes the high or the low is more significant. For example, the low demand projection for agricultural products indicates the surplus acreage that we might expect to have on our hands should the assumptions on which the low projection rest turn out to be the path of the future. It marks the outer limit of the range of problems that public policy may have to deal with.

Conversely, in the case of energy and some other materials, the high projection suggests the earliest date at which one or the other of the commodities involved might begin to show the effects, in terms of cost, of approaching depletion. Also, a projection that delivers a verdict of adequacy at all three ranges suggests quite a different degree of confidence or urgency for policy making purposes from one in which adequacy is indicated at only one or two levels.

The methodology employed in making these estimates may be

Selected Economic and Resource Estimates for 1980 and 2000

	1960	1980	2000
ECONOMIC AGGREGATES			
Population (millions)	180	245	330
Labor force (millions)	73	102	140
Households (millions)	53	73	100
GNP ($ 1960 billions)	503	1,060	2,200
GNP per worker ($ 1960)	6,900	11,500	15,500
Government expenditures ($ 1960 billion)	100	240	550
Private investment ($ 1960 billion)	73	150	320
Personal consumption expenditures ($ 1960 billion)	330	660	1,320
INTERMEDIATE PRODUCTS			
Meat consumed (billion lbs.)	29	46	65
Cotton produced (billion lbs.)	7.5	10.4	16
Autos produced (millions)	6.6	11.6	24
New dwelling units (millions)	1.5	2.7	4.2
Steel produced (million tons)	100	175	280
Construction lumber produced (billion bd. ft.)	31	48	79
Fertilizer consumed (million tons of nutrients)	8	21	42
BASIC RESOURCE REQUIREMENTS			
Cropland, including cropland pasture (million acres)	442	437	455
Forest land, commercial (million acres)	484	484	484
Grazing land (million acres)	700	700	700
Outdoor recreation land (million acres)	44	75	136
Urban land (million acres)	21	32	45
Timber (billion cu. ft.)	11	21	36
Fresh water withdrawals (billion gal./day)	250	340	480
Fuel (quadrillion BTU's)	45	83	138
Oil (billion bbls.)	3.2	5.3	9.7
Coal (million short tons)	398	607	698
Natural gas (trillion cu. ft.)	13.1	25.8	35.0
Iron ore (million short tons)	125	200	320
Aluminum, primary (million short tons)	1.8	7.8	19.5
Copper, primary (million short tons)	1.7	2.4	3.9

SOURCE: Taken from work in progress at Resources For The Future under the provisional title of *Resources in America's Future*. Medium level estimates only are shown.

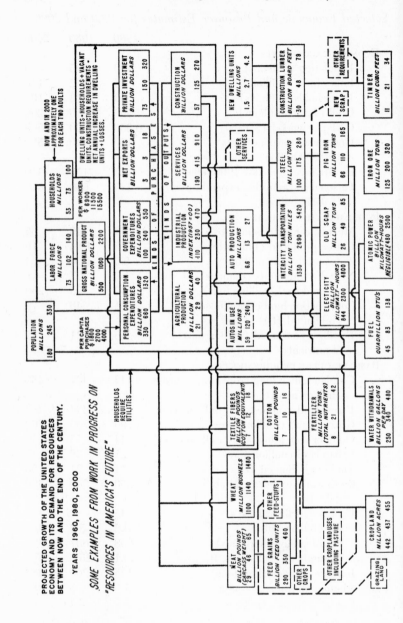

PROJECTED GROWTH OF THE UNITED STATES
ECONOMY AND ITS DEMAND FOR RESOURCES
BETWEEN NOW AND THE END OF THE CENTURY.

YEARS 1960, 1980, 2000

SOME EXAMPLES FROM WORK IN PROGRESS ON

"RESOURCES IN AMERICA'S FUTURE"

illustrated by examining briefly one particular chain of estimates stretching from the over-all economic projections through end-use projections to intermediate products and basic resources. The demand for housing (2.7 million new units in 1980, 4.2 million new units in 2000) is derived from the projections of population, its age distribution, family formations in particular years, income, and other characteristics. It is also related to supply factors, such as the age specific distribution of the housing stock, the likely replacement rate, upgrading and improvement of units, the possibility of new types of supply altogether such as second houses, and so on. Throughout, historical trends and relationships are employed for developing the future estimates.

The demand for the intermediate product, lumber, is derived from the demand in specific years for housing and other types of construction which require lumber. These in turn have been drawn from estimates of the demand for the end products into which these other uses of lumber flow. Generally speaking, the range in the demand estimates from high to low reaches its maximum at this intermediate product level, since the possibilities for materials substitution are greatest at this cross sectional level. Thus, we have had to come to terms statistically with the possibility of the substitution of steel, aluminum, tiles, plastic boards and the like for lumber, as well as of the substition of composition boards and paper products, both of which may be made of wood.

The final stage is to consolidate all the demands for the intermediate product, lumber, in such a way that these can be traced back to the demand on the forests. The other main strands of demand, in addition to lumber, are from pulp and paper products, plywood and composition board, railroad ties, pit props and poles, fuel wood, and several others. The over-all demand, expressed in cubic feet of wood, provides in rough form an estimate of how much wood will have to be cut in a given year, and with due allowance for amounts uncut, and uncuttable, and wasted, how much will have to be grown. More meaningful is the presentation of demand, not for the total amount of wood, but for the amount of timber required and growing stock suitable for the several major intermediate products.

Turning to the supply side, such factors have to be examined as the existing stock of sawtimber and other types of timber, differential growth rates among species and sections of the country, rates of cut, efficiency in processing and use, and other technical factors. Beyond this, attention has been given to the possibilities for imports and exports and, most difficult of all, the likely path of adjustment to cost and price changes. Over past years the cost and price of lumber, generally speaking, have been rising in this country relative to the cost and price of other construction materials, such as steel, aluminum, and cement.

Our perspectives on demand and supply of lumber for the future would indicate that in all likelihood the requirements we have calculated cannot be met on the basis of the contemporary supply pattern and practices, but only with sharp improvement in the utilization of existing forest lands. Failure to act undoubtedly would tend to raise the cost of the forest products, certainly of lumber. Even such actions as now seem possible would probably prove insufficient to check this tendency. Thus the past price trend is likely to continue.

It is obvious that this development would have its repercussions on the demand as we have projected it, but in our projection technique there is no provision for "feedback" to the demand projections from the judgment of adequacy — or lack thereof — through their effect on price. Rather, we consider the likely consequences of demand trends and supply outlook for the cost and price situation. The rate at which the use of substitute materials may increase is one of the unknowns; this depends largely on technological planning within the relevant sectors of industry and the rate at which the cost differential between lumber and its competing materials tends to increase.

Cost must here be understood in the widest sense, not simply in terms of dollars and cents per pound or square foot of material. Substitute materials typically permit the adoption of novel techniques in design and use. This affects the designer, the builder, the producer of construction materials, and, last but not least, the consumer who must be prepared to accept the consequences of change. Thus cost per physical unit is only the starting point but by no means the most pertinent standard of comparison.

The substitution rate depends also, of course, on improvements in forest management practices, conservation in the processing and use of lumber and other forest products, the possibilities for larger imports, and ultimately on developments in forest genetics and physiology which may result in hybrids that will grow trees much larger and faster.

In this construction-lumber-forest complex, as in others, the American economy is notable for its willingness to seek substitutions and new sources and to accommodate readily to them. This is fine for improving the economy but very hard on the making of accurate projections. This characteristic of substitution furnishes scope for technological planning and is the hallmark of an enterprising economy. A major objective of government policy is to stabilize this aspect of the economic environment at a high level through appropriate laws and regulations and to enhance thereby opportunities for creative forces of development and growth.

RESOURCE PROBLEMS AND PROSPECTS AHEAD

Our general conclusion drawn from this kind of a systematic demand and supply look ahead is that for several decades there will be general adequacy of resource and raw materials in this country *provided* there is no catastrophic war, *provided* there is a continued flow of education and research and a continued flow of technological innovation (including discovery, substitutions, conservation, and so forth), and *provided* access to sources in other countries remains open. The provisos are extremely important and will be examined later. Furthermore, the finding of general over-all adequacy does not mean that there will not be severe problems for particular materials at particular times and in particular places. Nor does it mean that sufficient supplies will be forthcoming without considerable effort in research, technological planning and development of many kinds, strenuous conservation efforts, and further improvements in management across the board. Indeed these problems will challenge the most imaginative thinking and effort of both business and government.

A few of the more important resource problems and opportunities ahead will be considered here; each presents challenges for technological planning.

Energy

Over the length of our national history, energy resources, while never altogether easy to win, have been ample to support rapid economic growth. Projection ahead in this field as in others is hazardous, but the picture which emerges from recent studies shows general adequacy — i.e., the meeting of projected demand without significant increases in real cost — at least until around 1980 for the various energy-using sectors of the economy (such as households, industry, and transportation) with supplies being drawn from substantially the present conventional sources.[2] This is in sharp contrast to the record of the past century during which the major source of energy for the economy has shifted sharply from a predominant reliance upon wood more than a century ago to coal at the end of the 19th century and lasting until after World War I, and since then to oil and gas which now supply 70% to 75% of the total.

Beyond 1980 to the end of the century the outlook has to be uncertain primarily because depletion, in the sense of rising cost, of the leading contemporary sources of energy — domestic crude oil and natural gas — is strongly indicated. Looking back at the history of crude oil supply and demand, one naturally hesitates to make such a judgment. Discovery of new deposits of oil has confounded every prophet who went on record predicting the early depletion of this resource since oil first flowed at Titusville. Yet it is beyond dispute that the amount of oil and gas in the ground is finite and it is likely, therefore, that at prospective rates of consumption, even in the face of optimistic assumptions regarding improvements in the technology of both discovery and recovery, cost of energy will begin to feel the effects of depletion of domestic oil-bearing formations before the century is out.

The response of the economy is less certain, for there are various evasive maneuvers on the horizon, some in direct substitution of oil and gas, some through indirect displacement. First of all, technology will undoubtedly postpone the effects of depletion through improvement in finding and recovery of oil and gas. Recent years have seen substantial improvements in secondary recovery techniques for underground oil. Given the attention now lavished on this technique and the fact that in the past pools have given up at most one-third of their content, there is good reason for anticipating that secondary recovery will continue to increase in importance and ten to fifteen years from now will supply per-

---

[2] The statistical background for this and the following paragraphs on energy is to be found in Schurr, Netschert, et al., *Energy in the American Economy 1850-1975* (Baltimore, Johns Hopkins Press, 1960), and in the forthcoming *Resources in America's Future*.

haps as much as one-third of the total consumption. But this will merely postpone, not prevent, depletion. Its effect on costs, in the longer run, may be mitigated or even offset entirely through the exploitation of shale and tar sands, the liquefaction or gasification of coal, and the use of nuclear and other unconventional forms of energy. Finally, world reserves of oil and gas — less explored and depleted than those in the United States — offer the possibility of supplementing domestic supplies, even though rising demand in the developing countries will undoubtedly claim a rising share of oil and gas throughout the world. Which particular combination of these elements will be the path of progress will largely depend upon relative advances in technology as these are reflected in cost, and upon institutional factors.

The possibilities for large-scale use of shale as a source of liquid fuels are very good. The research and pilot operations have already been carried out in the Colorado plateau. While there are problems of scale, location, water supply, and transportation, it appears evident that usable liquid fuels can be produced from shale at a cost of no more than 10% or 20% higher than liquid fuels from conventional underground sources. The development of tar sands, found in large amounts in the western prairies of Canada, while not as far advanced in terms of pilot plant operations, is widely believed to be at least an equally feasible source for large amounts of liquid fuels, held back principally by a serious locational handicap.

Economic conversion to liquid or gaseous form of one of our most abundant fuel resources, bituminous coal, which has been losing its markets for direct use as a solid fuel, is another goal toward which technology might well be oriented on a large scale. Success would make available, not in the Rockies or in the Canadian prairies, but in the heart of the country a long-term source of liquid fuel for which vast markets are likely to persist for decades. The know-how exists but the cost is presently prohibitive. A breakthrough here would both revive an ailing industry and secure the energy base of the economy for a long time to come.

Nuclear energy does not hold its greatest promise in substitution for liquid and gaseous fuels, and this seems to point to the need for technological planning which will, by some sidewise displacement process, permit nuclear energy to contribute toward meeting an incipient liquid fuel problem. For example, further development of use of nuclear-produced electricity in space heating could result in a saving on fuel oil and gas. Nuclear energy may be substituted on a wide scale in the propulsion of ships. Conceivably process heat from nuclear sources could be used in the extraction of liquid petroleum from oil shale. Direct use of nuclear energy for the propulsion of automobiles, buses, and trucks seems to present almost insuperable difficulties because of the need for heavy shielding, but it is possible that the indirect substitution process may take over. With further improvement of the fuel cell, powered by say hydrogen, and with the hydrogen produced with the aid of nuclear heat, it may become both technically and economically feasible to engineer a series of fuel cells for the purpose of moving automobiles and other land vehicles.

Further off in the distance are the possibilities for application of solar energy in certain uses. Conversely to nuclear energy, which is a very highly concentrated form of energy, solar energy is widely dispersed and has to be collected or concentrated if it is to become useful for new purposes. A far-ranging development program is now getting under way, and it is a distinct possibility that by the end of the century solar energy may have entered some parts of the economy in a significant way.

Figure 2 presents estimates of the demand picture for 1980 and 2000 (and actual figures for 1960) for the several energy commodities and indicates also the major uses to which they may be put. Technological planning may find some guidelines in this set of projections. In a sense the economy will have a breathing time for the next two decades during which conventional energy sources will suffice; thereafter, rather massive substitutions of new sources or techniques may have to take place if substantial cost increases are to be avoided. Discovery, research, and development programs, it would seem, may be laid out in a thoughtful and reasonably unhurried manner with the hope that they will produce results in about twenty years.

Water

Projections of the uses and sources of water supply can also furnish a framework within which technological planning in certain industries may operate more effectively. Unfortunately past statistics of water use, supply, and cost are very scant and do

PROJECTED ENERGY DEMAND, BY SOURCES AND ECONOMIC SECTORS

C	O	G	E-HN	AS	E-AS
COAL (INCLUDING AMOUNTS CONSUMED IN ELECTRICITY GENERATION)	OIL	NATURAL GAS	ELECTRICITY BASED ON HYDRO AND NUCLEAR SOURCES	ALL SOURCES (INCL. NGL, NOT SHOWN SEPARATELY)	ELECTRICITY FROM ALL SOURCES

(IN BTU x 10^{15})

SECTOR	1960						1980						2000					
	C	O	G	E-HN	AS	E-AS	C	O	G	E-HN	AS	E-AS	C	O	G	E-HN	AS	E-AS
RESIDENTIAL	1.6	2.7	3.7	0.4	8.6	2.0	2.8	2.5	7.2	1.8	14.6	5.4	2.7	1.8	7.2	5.3	17.2	9.1
COMMERCIAL	1.2	0.9	1.2	0.2	3.6	1.2	1.6	1.3	2.2	1.0	6.3	2.9	1.5	2.4	2.2	2.6	8.8	4.4
TRANSPORT	0.1	8.3	0.4	—	9.6	—	—	16.9	0.8	—	19.3	—	—	35.0	1.1	—	38.3	—
INDUSTRY	5.4	1.6	4.8	0.7	12.9	3.7	8.8	2.7	10.2	3.1	26.4	9.4	11.1	3.9	18.8	10.7	49.8	18.3
TOTAL (INCLUDING SECTORS NOT SHOWN)	10.4	18.0	13.6	1.6	45.5	8.8	15.9	29.8	26.7	6.9	83.5	20.9	18.3	53.4	36.2	21.3	138.0	36.4

Figure 2

not support future projections as well as one might wish. Furthermore, national projections of water demand and supply have far less meaning than regional or river basin projections, primarily because water cannot be transported from one basin to another in large amounts. For this reason a finding of over-all water adequacy for the whole country is not particularly meaningful or helpful. Further difficulties arise from such matters as the definitional difference between water that is withdrawn, used, and returned to streams and water that actually disappears in use through evaporation and transpiration. Figure 3 illustrates the outlook in a tentative way for two selected regions: the Ohio river region in the east and the Colorado in the west.

From this sample look-ahead several problems emerge clearly. The Colorado region, like most western regions with the notable exception of the Pacific Northwest, which is supplied adequately by the Columbia River, either faces water shortages already, or will face them in the near future. In the Colorado river basin, for example, water disappearance is already about 15 times the dependable flow (flow that is available 95% of the time), and water withdrawals exceed dependable flow by close to 30 times. It will be noted in Figure 3 that projected disappearance is about the same as average flow throughout the period shown, and even exceeds it slightly at times. Water supply on the average, therefore, is now fully used up or almost so, and the prospect is that this will continue. Additional dams and reservoirs and further regulation of flow can affect water use by raising the dependable flow which in turn can yield such benefits as increased hydroelectric capacity, but cannot affect average flow, which sets the upper limit over the long run to water disappearance. These observations about water disappearance in the Colorado make no allowance for maintaining some minimum amount of flow for diluting pollution which, though not now large compared to eastern rivers, will undoubtedly increase in the future. The upshot of all this, despite confusion caused by terminological and measurement difficulties, is that the Colorado region now faces a severe water shortage problem that may well handicap economic growth.

In the Colorado river basin, as well as in most of the other basins in the west, the largest water use is irrigation farming, averaging nearly 90% of total withdrawals over all the western

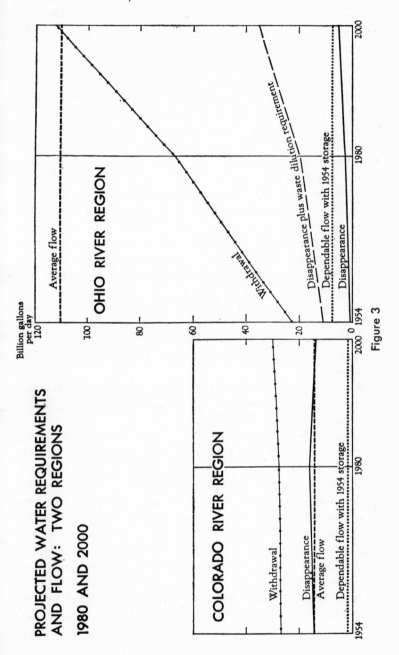

Billion gallons per day

PROJECTED WATER REQUIREMENTS AND FLOW: TWO REGIONS

1980 AND 2000

OHIO RIVER REGION

Average flow

Withdrawal

Disappearance plus waste dilution requirement

Dependable flow with 1954 storage

Disappearance

COLORADO RIVER REGION

Withdrawal

Disappearance
Average flow

Dependable flow with 1954 storage

Figure 3

regions. Recent economic research indicates that irrigation is a relatively low value use of water in the west as compared to industrial, municipal, and even recreation use of water. One study recently completed and now nearing publication focuses on the economics and alternative use of new water supply developed in the San Juan River of northwestern New Mexico. Under a variety of relevant and apparently realistic assumptions as to place and pattern of use, including the possibility for economic transmountain diversion of this supply to the Rio Grande valley for use in Albuquerque and the other more populated parts of the state, it turns out that water used in industry might have the effect of increasing state income as much as 40 times that of using the water for irrigation. Furthermore, use of the water for recreation might return six times as much in state income.[3]

This and other recent analyses point clearly to the main western water problem: that of shifting the emphasis in water use from irrigation to other uses, principally municipal, industrial, and recreational. These uses can support higher costs and prices for water supply; more jobs can be made available per unit of water used and more population can be supported; and, as an added bonus, most of the water used for such purposes is returned to streams whereas in agriculture some 60% actually disappears into the atmosphere.

Other measures may be taken to improve the western water picture. Research on water conservation across the board can yield major returns. One interesting possibility is the use of hexadecanol and other monomolecular film-forming substances, which spread rapidly and easily over the surface of reservoirs to reduce evaporation losses. The gains here can be very great; Lake Meade, formed by Hoover Dam on the Nevada-Arizona border, now suffers a loss of over 1 million acre feet each year from evaporation. A protective film could probably reduce this loss considerably, although experiments to date do not permit an accurate estimate of the feasible reduction. Other possibilities include the reduction of the number of phreatophytes, which are useless water-using plants and trees, further improvements in irrigation canal linings, vegetation control of the upland portions of river basins, and integrated management of surface and ground

[3] Nathaniel Wollman et al., *The Value of Water in Alternative Uses* (to be published by The University of New Mexico Press).

water. More physical and statistical research on artificially induced rainfall apparently is needed before anything definite can be said about this possibility.

In much of the eastern and middle part of the country the problem appears to be not so much one of sheer supply as one of supplying reasonably clean water. This characterizes the Ohio River region as shown in the chart. Despite fairly sizable efforts on the part of many municipalities to prevent and abate pollution, the problem seems to be gaining rather than receding in most places. Pollution takes a variety of forms including biological, chemical, and sedimentation. A recent preliminary study indicates that the requirement of water supplies to maintain minimum flows in eastern rivers, thereby flushing and moving sewage and other forms of pollution downstream into the salt water, may overwhelm all other uses within a few decades.[4] This possibility, or rather probability, shows up clearly in the chart on the continuously rising line of disappearance plus waste dilution requirement, most of which is the latter. These estimates are based on the maintenance of a standard of water purity of at least four parts of dissolved oxygen per million. Admittedly this is a rather high standard for highly populated industrial areas, but it seems consistent with good standards of public health, improved recreation, and the aesthetic desires of many people for clean water. Also it is quite feasible technically. Technological planning for the introduction and improvement of pollution treatment processes and for pollution prevention measures will undoubtedly have a high payoff in years to come; indeed these will be necessary if estimated future water requirements are to be met in a dependable way.

Other Resources

The same kind of story that has been presented in energy and in water can also be told in the other resource fields. One interesting and rather new possibility is to be found in the outdoor recreation field. As a result of a rapidly growing population, high levels and increases in income per family, greater mobility of people, and shorter work weeks and longer vacations, the amount of time and money spent in outdoor recreation has been increasing

[4] Nathaniel Wollman, *Water Supply and Demand*, Committee Print No. 32, U.S. Senate Select Committee on National Water Resources (Washington, Government Printing Office, 1960).

very rapidly during recent years. Statistics are scant, but they seem to point to a growth of somewhere between 6% and 10% annually in the use of outdoor recreation areas and facilities, ranging all the way from city parks and playgrounds to the magnificent national parks and forests. Indeed, outdoor recreation has become a large-scale, growth industry. Continuation of this rate of growth over the next few decades seems altogether likely.[5] It involves not only the direct use of land and water areas but numerous ancilliary industries, such as the small boat and outboard motor industries, outdoor sports equipment of many kinds, construction of summer homes at beaches, lakes, and in the mountains, and so on. Estimates of demand for outdoor recreation as affected by location, age and income distribution of the population, distances traveled, amounts spent, and the like can provide the basis for technological planning in industries related to this activity. The employment of certain standards of use, expressed in man-days of use per acre or per dollar of investment in facilities, or in some other way, makes it possible to translate anticipated demands into requirements for additional outdoor recreational acreage and facilities of many kinds, all of which call for technological planning and investment.

Similarly, a future demand-supply picture can be built up for the various metallic and nonmetallic minerals, agricultural crops, forest products, and chemical materials of various kinds. With few exceptions, our demand projections in the metal field point toward the continuing need for new discovery or, alternatively, for commercially feasible methods of using low-grade ores, if dependence upon foreign supplies is to be avoided. It is interesting in this connection that a few months ago we were visited by a representative of a major U.S. oil company who was seeking advice as to the likely future demand for various metals. His interest, it turned out, was motivated by the fact that his company's staff of geologists greatly exceeded the foreseeable need for their services in the oil business, and that the transfer of the technology they had developed in oil and gas exploration to metals exploration seemed a worthwhile investment. Ideas as

[5] See Clawson, Held, and Stoddard, *Land for the Future* (Baltimore, Johns Hopkins Press, 1960), Chapter III. Also Marion Clawson, "Methods of Measuring the Demand for and Value of Outdoor Recreation," Resources For The Future Reprint No. 10, 1959.

to future demand and supply can thus give the impetus to transfer of existing technology as well as to creation of new technology.

In the case of manganese, to illustrate more fully one of the metals for which this country is almost wholly supplied from foreign and generally remote sources, even the resource situation of the world as a whole is not such as to assure continued production for the balance of the century. Depicted in Figure 4 are world reserves, that is, the metal content that can be recovered at present levels of cost and technology, conjectural cumulative demand through the year 2000 at two different levels, and potential ore, that is, occurrences not now commercially minable. If the data reflect and project the situation at all correctly, then it is clear that technology must aim at three things: (1) facilitate discovery of additional reserves, (2) reduce the cost level at which potential ore, including that now accumulating in steel mill slag heaps, can be mined, or (3) tackle production of the nodules on the ocean floor which experts claim are even now within economic reach, provided venture capital of substantial magnitude can be attracted to this proposition. Failing progress along these paths, one must be prepared for a gradual increase in the cost and price of manganese around the world, and in the Free World above all.

As a final word along this line, it is interesting to note that the outlook for basic agricultural crops for the next decade or longer is for continued oversupply. In a sense, therefore, the future picture in agriculture is quite different from that for many of the raw materials. Even here, however, some clues for technological planning can be found. For example, what are the possibilities for new or increased use of basic agricultural crops in industry for the production of alcohol and fuel, fabrics and paper, and so on. In this paper we do not attempt to fill in the full picture for agricultural crops, metals, energy sources, water, or any other resources, but merely to indicate a few of the possibilities for the future.

Some Conclusions for Technological Planning

A number of promising lines for technological planning and resource development have been opened up in the preceding sections dealing with the resource trends and visible problems ahead. A more careful sighting in on these opportunities could result

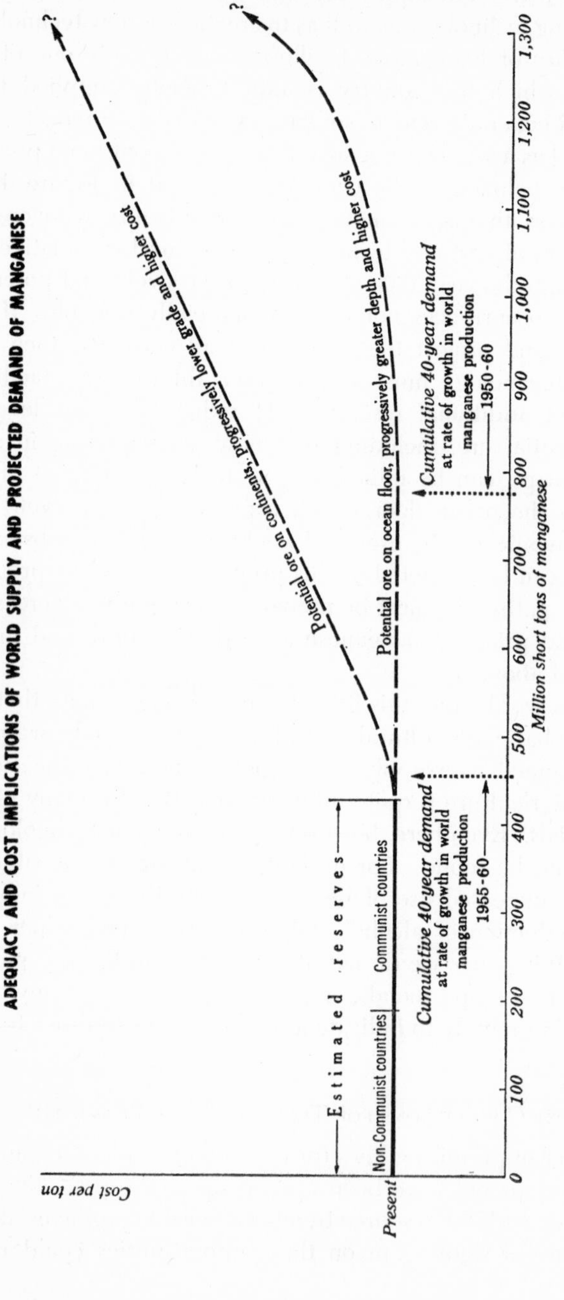
ADEQUACY AND COST IMPLICATIONS OF WORLD SUPPLY AND PROJECTED DEMAND OF MANGANESE
Potential ore on continents, progressively lower grade and higher cost
Potential ore on ocean floor, progressively greater depth and higher cost
?
?
Estimated reserves
Non-Communist countries
Communist countries
Cumulative 40-year demand at rate of growth in world manganese production 1955-60
Cumulative 40-year demand at rate of growth in world manganese production 1950-60
Cost per ton
Present
0
100
200
300
400
500
600
700
800
900
1,000
1,100
1,200
1,300
Million short tons of manganese

Figure 4

from a periodic review of the demand and supply projections, taking into account the effects of changing technology on the demand and supply outlook.

One thing that emerges clearly from this kind of a look at resource and raw materials in the American economy is the need to maintain and increase basic research in the physical, biological, and engineering sciences, and in economics and the other relevant social sciences.[6] For example, geological survey work must be continued and accelerated so that there is maximum chance that new ore bodies will be discovered. The same is true of hydrologic surveys which form the basis for water development. Research in entomology leading to the control and elimination of insects which are harmful to trees and crops has enormous potential for increasing the supplies. Genetic research in both agricultural plants and trees holds promise of large augmentations to supply in the more distant future. For example, physiological and genetic research done during recent years with the pines (some of which has been supported by Resources For The Future) indicates that as we come to understand more about the flowering and germination of the trees and the possibilities for hybrid strains, we may expect considerably more rapid timber growth over many of our forest areas. Research in solid state physics is opening the way to "molecular engineering" of essentially new construction and other materials by means of which strength, durability, and other characteristics may be greatly improved in relation to volume and weight. Other work in molecular physics holds the promise of developing monomolecular films which can be spread on the surface of reservoirs to reduce evaporation losses. Research and development for desalinization of sea water and brackish water are now proceeding on a fairly wide scale under government auspices. As more information is derived from pilot plant operations of several types, significant cost breakthroughs may be achieved.

Research is needed also in the social sciences and can be expected to pay off handsomely. In economics, basic research is

[6] Total research and development expenditures have increased some threefold since 1953 and now are running about $14 billion a year. For trends in research (basic and applied) and development expenditures during recent years, see various publications and releases of the National Science Foundation.

needed in methodology for estimating impact of specific technological innovations in specific industries and regions, and on
related activities. There would be important gains if the demand-
supply projections framework outlined earlier in this paper could
be improved and re-done periodically, say every three years, by
an agency of the government. This makes up the economic and
resource framework within which technological development
takes place; it should be elaborated and maintained. Benefits and
costs of research itself need much more profound examination
than they have been given thus far, as do the estimating of benefits and costs of particular development projects and sequences
of projects.

Research has to be fed not only with funds but also, and most
important, by a stream of highly educated and motivated young
men and women. Educators and scientists, almost unanimously,
have been calling for more such persons and for a higher quality
training. Without increased attention to this factor the whole
process of technological planning will not be adequately sustained.

A few additional selected lines for technological planning and
resource development may be indicated, each of which offers
promise for the more distant future. It is always risky to place
too high a bet on any one such line; on the other hand, it is even
more risky for a business firm that wants to maintain and improve
its position over the future to neglect these less certain possibilities. On the horizon in the energy field, for example, exciting work
is being done on various types of fuel cells, magnetohydrodynamics, thermionics, secondary and tertiary oil recovery, and
nuclear energy, as well as along more conventional lines. In the
minerals field one may mention improvements in steel making
through the replacement of air blasts by oxygen and even direct
reduction, the possibilities of getting nodules of manganese and
phosphates from the ocean floor, and the development and use of
semiconductor ceramic materials. In the water field a scanning of
the horizon shows many possibilities in water conservation as
noted earlier, in the recycling of water in industrial processes and
the substitution of air fin for water cooling, long-distance and
transmountain transportation of water, the integrated management of surface and underground water, and better sequence and
timing of projects in river basin development. In forestry quick

burning and other new techniques for control of less desirable species is but one example of technological planning leading to improved management of a basic resource. In wood products, new particle boards, precut lumber for modular construction, and the like offer economies.

For these and other "farther out" possibilities an emphasis on basic research becomes of highest importance. A portion of each research and development budget could well be devoted to the more remote and "off beat" projects, as well as to the basic understandings from which new insights arise.

Obviously the fuel that keeps the engine of technological development running is an expanding, high-quality program of education and training in the engineering schools and the industrial training centers. Without this the rate of advance cannot be maintained, let alone increased. This is true in resource fields as in others. Enough has been spoken and written on this subject that it needs no further attention here.

A final point needs to be made explicitly. Technological planning for natural resource and raw material development may be done in terms of the United States, North America, the western hemisphere, or the world. It would probably be possible to operate an advanced economy within the United States or North America alone, but the costs would be high. Low-grade taconite, concentrated at high cost, might have to be substituted for richer imported ores, if the United States alone as a source of iron supply is considered. Similarly, alumina would have to be extracted from domestic clays. Manganese, nearly all of which is now brought in from overseas, would have to be mined at perhaps five times the cost from domestic sources, refined from tailings, or got up off the floor of the sea in nodules. Synthetic products would have to be substituted for industrial diamonds, and although the man-made product is in some respects an improvement over nature's, this is by no means universally true. Tin in tin cans would have to be replaced entirely by glass bottles and paper cartons as scrap recycling diminished. Tea and chocolate would disappear from the table, and so would coffee unless Latin American sources were retained. Tourist travel abroad would die out.

Furthermore, the United States depends on export markets overseas for one-third to two-fifths of its cotton, wheat, rice, and tobacco production; for only a slightly smaller but growing share in food fats and oils; and for substantial amounts of its exports of machine tools, electrical equipment, and other highly processed items. Elimination or drastic reduction of the United States export trade would severely dislocate large segments of the domestic economy; it would interrupt industrial advance and gains in living levels in other countries with most serious repercussions politically as well as economically.

In practical terms, therefore, it is out of the question to undertake either natural resource projections or technological planning in this field except on a scale which includes international trade and investment in raw materials. Anything less would greatly aggravate the resource problems of the United States for the foreseeable future.

Q. You spoke of the possibility of a lumber demand going from, I believe, 31 to 79 billion board feet and you commented that you didn't think this was going to be possible with our current way of doing things. We're also acquainted with another study made by the Stanford people in which they give some figures that give the opposite picture: that in the long run we will not be using as much lumber; that lumber as we know it will possibly be off, I think, by about 6%. So I wonder if you'd comment on how we get these diametrically opposed viewpoints from people who are supposedly looking at the same basic data?

F. (Fisher) This doesn't surprise us, of course, that different "experts" looking at the same data come up with a different view. This is the spice of our existence in business and in economics. Partly, I think it's methodological and partly not. I have not examined the Stanford study very recently, and perhaps you have.

We, very purposefully, have followed a methodology which does not close up the gaps that are incipient when demand, say, exceeds supply. Obviously, as you move forward through time, these gaps do close. Looking back, supply always equals demand. We have chosen a methodology which will open the gap to the fullest possible view because this is an indication of an emerging problem. The more difficult the problem looks in these terms, the more necessary it is for somebody to do something about it in the direction of substituting aluminum or steel or tiles; or in substituting lower-grade lumber, composition boards, and so forth, for high-grade lumber; or in directing attention away from those products that embody a lot of lumber. It's in the methodology, probably, that the main difficulty comes. And our methodology is not the same as theirs.

L. (Landsberg) Yes, this is largely so. I could outline various provisions under which you could come closer. There's one particular point that I might use to illustrate this point: if you assume a geographic shift in timber production from the east to the west, that is, when a higher percentage is lumber from the west than is now the case, you come much closer to closing the gap. How fast you can do this realistically is a problem. At the same time, unless you assume substantial changes in management, in fire prevention, and in disease prevention, in other words, in forestry technique, you can see that your cumulative drain will almost exceed your forest supply by the year 2000, if your demand continues unchecked in that direction. We know that one of two things will happen. Either price will go up and discourage demand and we will have substitution, or we will be forced into a large-scale program of improvement in forest management. This is the kind of thing I tried to point out. To pick one figure, at which we think in a given year demand and supply will come together, is not as important to us as identifying the problems involved.

F. I might add this: In this case and in many others the national picture is not too revealing. You have to get down to regional terms. This is obviously true in the case of water demand and supply. It happens also to be true in the lumber-timber complex. The big reserves presently are in the west; mature timber that no longer is growing very much. The rapid growth is in the east in second and third growth, where the young trees just grow faster. A kind of rational approach looking at it in these broad terms would be to continue lumbering in the west, clear out the trees that aren't growing very fast to make way for young growth, and then move to the east. But these adjustments are difficult and all we've done is, we hope, to enrich understanding of the general situation within which business can maneuver and change can take place.

Q. Dr. Fisher, as an economist would you consider it the government's duty to do something about this?

F. Well, I don't accept the "government" as implied in the way you put the question. The government is us. It is business; it is labor; it is everybody in the political sense. It may well be that additional government policy and investment will be called for. This is not to say that strenuous effort may not also be called for from business. My own bias is in favor of the business system handling it to the extent possible, but I don't see a dichotomy really. The busines system, I hope, will close the gaps within an improved framework of government policy. Now this could lead us into quite a discussion and so I'll stop with that.

Q. I'd like to question the things you said ought to be questioned; that is, the assumptions of leaving the feedback out. And it goes a little bit like this: If you leave the international feedback out, as you said you did for the energy study in which we needed only relatively crude data, won't we run into just a simple assumption? That the population growth in the rest of the world is equal to that of the United States right now? That the standard of living will become what the United States standard of living is today? . . . which are fairly reasonable asumptions. Then we come out with some very drastic differences on these energy reserves from those that you show. And I don't think we can estimate the reserves because the spread we found in our company studies, from the optimistic to the pessimistic, gives a range of answers from ten to one.

F. Let me say one thing. In the generalization we made about general adequacy of energy supply we meant it to apply to this country *with the proviso* that we import about what we do now. But now —

Q. We're on my thesis of why we ought to put the feedback in. Isn't this kind of sticking your head in the sand and saying that you automatically have to be —

F. Let us take the energy case and, if you like, put in some of the feedbacks in terms of discoveries, reserves, and possibilities in other parts of the world.

L. In this energy instance we have considered the international scene in terms of what might happen through forty years of consumption. Will there be anything for us even if we want it and at what price? This is the problem, I presume, that you are referring to. We have a very nasty problem trying to figure out what the rest of the world can consume in the next forty years.

As for the ranges of estimates, they don't particularly upset us; we present the low, medium, and high figures not in order to indicate margins of error or to be optimistic or pessimistic. The figures are not that at all. They are simply results of different assumptions — different possible paths. We think the medium figure is most likely, but neither the low nor the high is unlikely. A range of this kind is not indicative of how much our estimates may be off. Rather we say that, under a different set of assumptions which we outline, it may even go that high or that low. So, in this respect, this "high" is not as frightening.

Q. No, it's not frightening, but you kicked a number around on energy. Wouldn't the people in this room have to take your figure into account before they retire or not take it into account? This becomes important, because you've got to project such findings in terms of whether this is something that's going to happen in your lifetime or not happen in your lifetime.

Q. What complicates the picture much more is the current international military situation. This has placed a fairly high technical price on energy plans, and this is going to spur the development of power reactors.

Q. I question your 1975 figure on nuclear energy. Isn't it low?

L. Not really when you look at it in terms of presently installed capacity and the time it takes to make a real dent in it through additions of plant. I might say our estimate for the year 2000 might be of interest. It is that roughly 50% of all electrical energy would then be nuclear energy. This, in turn, is barely 15% of all energy consumed. In terms of this projection for the year 2000 of total energy, you don't get far by 1975 in nuclear energy and even by 2000 not as far as one might offhand be tempted to anticipate.

Q. I notice you gave transportation no credit at all . . .

F. Yes, but again shipping is a very small part of energy consumption. It's the advantage of this sort of across-the-board analysis that you can really afford to concentrate on the important things. You don't have to worry too much about the small fields.

THE NEXT HUNDRED YEARS

EDWARD TELLER

EDWARD TELLER

Professor of Physics-at-Large
Lawrence Radiation Laboratory
University of California
Berkeley, California

Dr. Teller was born in Hungary and educated in Germany, receiving his Doctor's degree at the University of Leipzig in 1930. He followed a career of scientific research and teaching in Europe until 1935, when he came to the United States to become Professor of Physics at the George Washington University and later at Columbia University. In 1942-1946 he was a physicist at the Manhattan Engineer District. From 1946-1952 he was Professor of Physics at the University of Chicago. During the last three years of this period he was on leave as the Assistant Director of Los Alamos Scientific Laboratory. Since 1953 he has been associated with the University of California in various capacities.

Dr. Teller's research work has resulted in important contributions to chemical physics, molecular physics, nuclear physics, and quantum theory. His scientific memberships, honors, and awards are almost too numerous to detail. In recent years, he has played an important part in decisions as to the feasibility of applying thermonuclear principles to weapons systems and to controlled thermonuclear power. His role as a scientist, scientific director, and scientific advisor to political bodies has given him a unique position and experience in technological planning on questions of global importance.

The Next Hundred Years

There is no doubt in my mind that the most inert substance known in the world is the human brain. It certainly has the greatest inertia, except possibly the association of many human brains. You will find that this phenomenon is so in the business world. You will find that this is so also in the military world. And you will find, I can assure you, that this is so in the scientific world. From what I have heard about this conference, it addresses itself to the most important problem — to try to fight this inertia and to loosen us up for the purpose of looking into the future.

I was asked to talk to you about prediction of the future. I am willing to do that because by the time the future comes along what I have predicted won't matter because I won't be here with you then. I may not be here at all by that time, and you certainly will have forgotten what I have said. It is one of the safest occupations in the world — to be a prophet. Usually it is considered to be safer to be a historian and talk about the past. In actual fact, however, to be a historian is much more dangerous, because if I say something wrong about history you'll catch me right away. I will, since I like to do the absurd, start therefore my talk about the future by talking to you about this dangerous subject — the past. And then, on that basis, I would like to look into the future, at least for a short distance. I would like to talk about the process, about the rapidly changing process, the industrial revolution which has carried the human race along at a speed which is really incredible.

To begin with, I would like to mention to you a little bit of unreliable statistics about the growth of homo mis-named sapiens. There were, I am told, in the year 10,000 B.C. approximately a hundred thousand of our ancestors around. Then when the Pyramids were built this number had increased to several million. By the time of the Roman Empire the number was a hundred million and after that came a period of decline and stagnation in number. Such periods occurred before. If you look at the whole development on a really big scale, you could express the results roughly by saying that the number of people has approximately doubled once every thousand years.

149

Around 1650 something started to happen. In 1650, if I remember correctly, there were approximately 250 million people. In 1750 there were 500 million. In 1850 there was one billion, doubling not in every thousand years, but in every century. By the middle of our present century even this rate of growth was exceeded. There are now almost three billion of us and predictions as to numbers estimate, unreliably, that by 2050 there will be approximately ten billion people.

What I want to emphasize is that something happened in 1650 that changed everything. I can't tell you what caused this change; I'll just be discursive and say what happened before and what happened after, why I don't know.

By 1650 the world had started to move. You know that navigators had satisfied their curiosity of what happened if you went to the edge of the world and tried to fall down. You know that the simple old concepts of the earth sitting still and the crystal firmament of heaven enclosing everything, that these had been shaken by 1650. In the world of politics Europe was just getting out of a most horrible war — the Thirty Years War —which left Central Europe with 30% of its previous population. At the same time in France, Louis XIV started to reign for eighty long years and the conservative English chopped off the head of their king. India and China had been taken over by northern invaders, Koreans and Mongols respectively, and big dynasties were getting going in both of these places that were more brilliant, more powerful by far, than anything known in Europe. By the efforts of the navigators the American continent was drawn into the sphere of European thinking and European economy.

Now what happened in this first hundred years I am going to talk about — 1650-1750? I will not try to tell you everything. I want to be brief; as brief as I can be. There were a few really big things that happened and I want to concentrate on those. One thing that happened was Newton. We know the things that he did so well that we have completely forgotten what reality seemed to be in the pre-Newtonian days. He introduced a brand new revolutionary concept, the concept of universal law. Before him there was one law on earth — everything had its place and wanted to stay at rest; the heavy substances below, the lighter above. And there was another law in heaven —things were perfect and the rule was not rest but perfect motion, circular motion.

The idea of Newton was that the laws here on earth are precisely the same as the laws anywhere in the universe. This in itself is a more important accomplishment for our thinking than all other detailed discoveries of Newton's time.

This was not the only progress in science. During this century Linnaeus established a system of living beings and gave names to animals and plants which we are still using. The microscope extended our knowledge about living beings into a completely new world.

There also occurred a certain important development in technology. I would bet not more than three people here have heard about it. England ran out of firewood, they had burned too much of it. And, because of that, they had to turn to a poor and dirty substitute: coal. It was soon found that coal burned at a higher temperature and that you could now handle iron very much better than you could handle it before. The price of iron came down below that of bronze. The iron age really started at that time because prior to that iron could be used only for some particularly important purposes, like art or war. Newton's discoveries made it possible to dream of machines, and the accident of coal's having been introduced in England made it economically possible to construct these machines. All this had in fact no consequences in the century in which these events took place. What happened in politics was that the religious intolerance which had killed two out of three people in Central Europe had become very much milder and the European society much more stable and secure. In 1650 the Ottoman Empire was still menacing all of Europe. In 1750 Europe was without any doubt the strongest entity in the world.

In the next century, from 1750 to 1850, the Industrial Revolution actually occurred. But its roots go back firmly at least a hundred years before that. In the years 1750 to 1850 these various elements were brought together: The laws of physics which had been understood, the cheap metal which had been produced, and a tolerant society in which individuals could act with some initiative. It would be pointless to try to remind you how greatly this has changed the world.

I will say, however, something about the political developments which happened at the same time. Two things of overwhelming significance happened in politics. One was that the power of

Europe was extended over the whole globe. This was the start of the development of what we now know as the colonial system. Europe integrated the world, moved the world, and, at the same time, sowed the seed of more trouble than anyone could have foreseen.

The second great development was the French Revolution. This revolution established the idea of a national state. The Napoleonic wars were fought in the name of that national state. The peace which followed tried to get back to the good old days. But, even after the Vienna Congress, the national state stayed there and it was clear that this dynamic, rapidly developing, self-centered, and basically anarchic idea would cause more trouble in the future.

In addition to the French Revolution, there was another very much less significant revolution — the American Revolution. It was a more constructive revolution. And it created something — our country. In 1838 one of my favorite authors, de Tocqueville, wrote a wonderful study: *Democracy in America*. At the end of the first volume de Tocqueville makes a prediction. Of all the predictions I have ever read it is the most remarkable. He first states that on the North American continent a nation will live — 150 million people — speaking one language, having the same homogeneous institutions, worshiping in one pattern. This is no prediction; it was pretty obvious to say this. But he picked the time, and the time was approximately 1950 because this was the time when there were about 150 million of us. The remarkable statement follows at that point. Because de Tocqueville foresees what will happen by 1950. And he says this: All nations in 1838 have stopped developing or are proceeding with extreme difficulty. There are only two nations which are going ahead with ease and celerity — Russia and the United States of America. These two nations are very different. The Russian fights man; the American fights nature. The tool of the Russian is centralized authority and servitude. The instrument of the Anglo-American is the enterprise of the individual and freedom. The paths of the two are different, but each of them is destined by the will of heaven to sway half the globe. The prediction is for 1950 — and here the prophet ceases to speak.

What happened during that century 1750-1850 in science? In that century the number of people on the globe doubled. So did scientific knowledge and technical knowledge double. New sciences were put forth. Think of chemistry. The confusion and the secrets of alchemy were replaced by a rational, effective tool. Think of electricity and magnetism. In 1750 it consisted of parlor tricks. Around 1850 Faraday could make the modest and prophetic answer when he was asked by a member of parliament: "What good is this toy that you are demonstrating?" His reply was: "Someday you may tax this toy." In biology the theory that we are composed of cells was recognized and Lamarck tried to spin theories about how the giraffe got his neck. A more famous person made a voyage in the Pacific and started to make notes which actually were published in the next century.

Darwin did to us what Newton did to the earth. He made out of the living world a whole where we humans no longer stand apart as something really different in kind. We are so deeply involved in this theory of evolution that it is hard for us to remember that, only a hundred years ago, this sounded like heresy. I should prefer to spend the next three hours talking about the wonderful century from 1850 to 1950.

One thing that happened at the beginning of that century, stimulated by Darwin's discoveries, was the flowering of the materialistic philosophy. It tried to explain everything in the world on the basis of a machine-like behavior of everything that is around us. In a way it was a most impressive theory. But in a way also, it had a weakness in an entirely unexpected spot. The weakness of materialistic philosophy is that the materialistic philosophers had no inkling of what matter is. And before the end of the century, strangely enough, we did find out very much more about matter. In particular, we learned in atomic theory that the smallest parts of matter are unpredictable — are subject to laws of probability. If any one of us wishes to believe that the future is uncertain, and I certainly wish to believe it, there is no fact in physics to contradict it. We have learned indeed that causality, the iron law of cause and effect, is valid wherever you deal with large and homogeneous masses like a machine or like economic activities of very many people. But where you talk about the individual atoms or individual people the laws are quite different.

Nor was this the only surprise. When we look at the big things — into space — we learn that on this big scale time and space have an entirely different structure from what philosophers had been preaching from the beginning of history. And it turned out that in a strange way time and space are exceedingly similar to each other.

The new knowledge was put to practical use in a remarkable way. Today we can travel to the end of the world and come back in the time that people used in 1850 to go to the neighboring state. We can transmit information from continent to continent in a time much shorter than the time that is needed or ever will be needed to understand this information. We have unfortunately invented things like automobiles, television, and atomic explosions, each of which carries with itself its more or less obvious dangers.

And what did rapid progress do to politics? At first people may have believed that human progress, peace, and safety were compatible with one another. Then in the 20th century we have witnessed two devastating wars, and now we are involved in a situation about which nobody can think without some sense of very real worry.

I want to remind you that our knowledge is multiplying as fast or faster than our population. And I want, therefore, to impress upon you that what will come will be just as different or more so.

What will happen in the next decades? I will start with science. And, of course, to make predictions about science is the most impossible of all impossibilities, because the nature of scientific progress is surprise. If something were not surprising, we would already have invented it. In physics, in my own field, we have arrived, by understanding the atom, at an essentially complete description of what a piece of metal is, what a piece of wood is, what any other material — gas, liquid, or soap bubble — is. We have not understood everything. When we tried to divide the atom, we always got new things. A logical, complete, systematic understanding of the world is still not with us, nor does one know that it ever will be. We have managed to discover the approximate probable size and age of the universe, but when you try to get back and see how it all started, we have so far much too few clues. Scientists are trying to find whether the whole world can be considered as something logical and necessary as geometry. We have not succeeded, but this is the natural state of science and the scientists are a group of people who share with each other the completely irrational belief that what now seems to be confusing will in the future somehow become logical and simple.

There are other questions which may seem more urgent. One is "What am I?" If I look at myself from a materialistic point of view, I can tell you in very few words what I am. I am a little matter and an incredible amount of purposeful complication. I am nothing but an assembly of molecules. One cannot help but feel that, in the next period, we'll find out a lot more about complications and we might understand what life is or else we might find some remarkable reason why we should never have asked this question. But there is a different side to this whole problem, which to my mind is even more disturbing. I am fully aware of the fact that I am talking about exceedingly disturbing things. I have asked: What is life? What is consciousness? What is thought? The fact is that we are making great progress in constructing thinking machines; I am not using the word frivolously. I shall tell you precisely in what sense I am using this word. I can try and you can try and all of us have tried to describe the thinking process in explicit terms: This is the way a mathematician will reason. This is the way an economist will reason. This is the way, in a rational manner, I would make a decision even in a game of chess. I even may say that this is the way I will try to judge what kind of rhyme I should have put down when I want to write poetry.

All of this has been talked about with some measure of success. To the extent that any of this can be sharply formulated, I can make a machine do it. I can make the machine do it faster and better than anyone else. You may say a machine will always be machine-like. There is no element of chance in the working of machines. Let me tell you this is complete nonsense. I can instruct the machine: "You will make a random choice and write down one of the figures 1 to 10 and it is up to you which one you will write down. You will do it in such a way that one cannot predict what you are going to write down." You may say a machine can't learn. Nonsense. I can tell the machine: "Repeat this type of process many times with certain variations. You will judge the outcome, good or bad, according to a criterion which I shall define. According to the outcome, you will then continue to function in the way which will lead to the favorable outcome." In this way one can make a machine which will learn. The moment you have described explicitly and sharply what you mean by a mental process, the machine can do it. This opens an almost infinite. number of possibilities. Because we either will learn what thinking is, or, by exploring thoroughly those parts in thinking which we can describe, we might gain some conception of whether there is something inherently human in thinking. I am clearly talking about something I don't know and, of course, most of the really interesting things are the things we do not know.

What kind of an effect will all this have on the technical development of the world and on society? Let us start with our affluent society in America. We have found that people can work, cooperate, function effectively, even if they are not driven by the whip. We have found that, without forcing people to work, you can make people work together, incredibly efficiently and in a way that everyone is reasonably satisfied. We have arrived at this state which, from the point of view of a hundred years ago, is so near to paradise that it is hardly possible to tell the difference.

In this paradise there are some terrible problems. These machines that I mentioned might soon do the thinking for us and thinking may become obsolete. There might be a certain new and strange recurrence of technological unemployment among the intelligentsia. Somehow the world has become too good for us.

But let us talk about the whole world, not just about the United States of America, but the other two or three billion people. Among these it is safe to say that two billion people have felt the effects of the Industrial Revolution only in two ways. One is that relatively simple measures of hygiene have caused a fairly rapid multiplication, a population explosion. And the other is that these same people who live as miserably as we think no person should live, these people know that a different kind of life is possible. They want to have it — not in 2050, but today. This creates a problem. The fact that we happen to have written in our Constitution that all men are created equal means that we have signed a blank check which now seems to be presented for payment.

It would be good if, between the affluent and the needy, a third did not exist. But the third does exist: Communism and, very particularly, Communist Russia. Their world is based on precisely the opposite of our experience: People can and should be driven by the whip. They have created an empire which at present includes half the world and which they have clearly and explicitly said will include soon the whole world. Let me say that what I am talking about here has little or nothing to do with the difference between communism and capitalism. The essential part of the difference was put down on paper and published by de Tocqueville at a time when Marx already was alive but didn't have a beard yet. This difference, which is firmly based on history and which could be predicted by an acute political observer more than a century ago, will not disappear overnight by Khrushchev's taking over from Stalin or by some people sitting around a conference table.

What we should do is to look at the consequences which these different approaches led to. In Russia you have a fast development and some people say that Russian progress is much faster than ours. Our economy is increasing 3% a year; theirs is increasing 7% a year. I want to look at it differently; I think this comparison is pointless. While we have been going along at our slow pace we have also happened, not sufficiently but yet effectively, to help western Europe. Recovering from the ruins of the Second World War, western Europe lives now better and more peacefully than it ever did before. Eastern Europe, on the other hand, has been kept down on the same level where it was at the end of the Second World War, which was a very low level. And eastern Europe is treated now by Russia as a colonial country, as a colonial region. If you take western Europe and America together, on the one hand, and eastern Europe and Russia together, on the other hand, the progress in the two places is not very different. The miracle is that, using all this tremendous energy, all this incredible sacrifice, the Russians did not manage to progress faster than they did. I think that, insofar as we consider simply the rate of progress in a peaceful competition, we have nothing to worry about.

Russia is in so many ways the precise counterpart of a thoroughly imperialistic community. There is the whip and there is the military preparation. There is the will to conquer the world and there is the definite plan to channel every bit of progress that they make toward conquering the rest of the world economically or by military force, whichever happens to be the best or the most feasible. Starting from a rather weakened condition, the military power of Russia has become a most dangerous instrument. In their conventional force, in their submarine force, in their rockets, and now in their atomic weapons, they are stronger than we are. I am not worrying about hundred megaton explosions. I am worrying about the fact that the Russians have resumed testing and thereby made it quite clear that they are not very much interested whether we test or not. There is every sign that Russia today in the atomic age is stronger than we are militarily in every one of the areas which really counts.

I have so far talked about things I know. I will now become unreasonable and will talk about the things that I wish. We have to act in the world as it stands today. There is a problem — the revolution of rising expectations in the backward nations. There is a developing technology which can satisfy their needs, and I will tell you how. In a very few words I can project some ideas to you which might give you, not by their specific direction but by their size, an image of the future possibilities. Peaceful use of nuclear explosives makes it possible to change geography, to make a harbor, to build a canal where you want it, to bring water into arid regions by blasting passages through mountains, to uncover ore bodies, and thereby not just to add to the raw material resources but literally to multiply the raw material resources.

In a few years we'll predict weather. Beyond that we shall find out — this is very probable — how to change weather. And then we will have lost the last safe topic of conversation. Because what we will do to the weather influences Russia. What they will do to the weather will influence us. And we will live peacefully ever after only if we find a way to use our new knowledge to our mutual benefit.

We have hardly touched the richest resource of organic life — the cradle of life — the ocean. We are going after the fish with Stone Age methods. We have bred new species. Why can we not use fish the way we use cattle? Prepare for them the proper meadows of algae and breed a species which will swim into the nets when the harvest comes. It could be done. To do the same thing on land — it took thousands of years — but we have seen by this strange method of scientific thinking what our inert brains produced. Inventions can be infinitely stepped up, but who will do it? To whom do the oceans belong? There is a need, and the need cannot be satisfied without purposeful international cooperation.

There are two ways to accomplish all of this: The simple old foolproof method, the Russian method. This method is the use of power. It has worked for millennia. There is, however, a more modern method — our method. Let's talk it over, let's do it without a whip, let's do it willingly. How a lawful community can be built without a war, without the use of force, I do not know. I am quite sure that it cannot be done unless we have the power, unless we have the force. I hope it can be done without using that power and without using that force, but only if we have a really unprecendented amount of imagination or unselfishness and willingness to change.

I promised you that I will predict the future. In twenty or thirty years the world will be a most terrible place to live in — with the very idea of freedom of speech thoroughly forgotten, with no respect for the individual. This is one possibility. Or the world will be a place so much better that we today can hardly imagine that this can happen. But it must happen if we are to prevent the other possibility. The prediction I have to make is that, in a very short and foreseeable time, the world will be infinitely better or infinitely worse than it is now.

I will finish this talk by giving to you a couple of definitions which I like and which have a lot to do with these two predictions. The definition of the pessimist and the optimist. The pessimist is a person who is always right, but does not get any enjoyment out of it. And an optimist is a man who imagines that the future is uncertain and, therefore, feels that it is his responsibility to do something about it.

Q. Dr. Teller, I'd like to ask what our policy with respect to civilian defense should be in order that your more optimistic prediction could come true.

A. So far we have spent on civilian defense one-tenth of one percent out of every tax dollar. This seems to be too little. In a time when there is little doubt that the Russians are far ahead of us in the more dangerous weapons, we should try to do something about real defense. If we spent approximately one-tenth of our military budget on civilian defense, we could do a number of very important things. We could build adequate shelters for our whole population in a few years. These shelters will not guarantee the life of everybody who is in the shelter, but they will save many lives. In all probability 90% of our people can be saved. This will still be a terrible catastrophe to be avoided at any reasonable cost.

Why did we fail to develop adequate shelters? For two reasons: One is because discouraging statements have been made and widely repeated and widely believed. I will quote a famous statement: Man holds in his mortal hands the power to destroy all forms of human life. Most of us have heard it, most of us have accepted it, yet it happens not to be true. We do not have that power, nor will we acquire it, nor will anybody else acquire it in the foreseeable future. Because we have been so discouraged by these predictions of gloom, we have not tried to do the simplest thing and build shelters. And, if we are attacked today, all forms of human life will not end and our present civilization will not end. But the United States of America and freedom will be wiped out.

The other reason we did not do anything about it is that the question has been raised: What will happen after the attack? All our cities will be in ruins, those who will survive will starve, we cannot maintain our government in any case. I say this is nonsense. If we are willing to do a certain number of important things, we can survive as a nation and we can survive in better shape than anybody else.

First we need the shelters, second we need the stockpiles of food, and we need stockpiles of industrial machines. If we were to distribute our wheat surplus and other agricultural surpluses in such a way that these things would be usable in an emergency, that alone will give us a tremendous advantage over Russia. And what we need more is an organization so that, if the dreadful rainy day comes, each one of us will know his duties, to whom he reports, what to do in order to save lives and get the reconstruction of the country started. The best economic evaluations I have seen show that our country could be rebuilt in five years. But we cannot do it unless we have more than our ten fingers to start with and unless we have an organization which will continue to function. If we did these elementary things about civilian defense, I believe the Russians, who are rational, will never attack us. The greatest importance in civilian defense is not that it will tide us over a very difficult period. It's a very important argument, but not the main argument. The main argument is that, if we plugged this greatest loophole in our defenses, then probably war will never come and civilian defense will never be actually used.

Q   Is there any useful activity that all of us as individual enterprises can do in this event? You describe the national effort. Short of that, is there anything we can do?

A. I am quite sure that everyone can make his contribution. Civil defense is not the sole responsibility of our national government. Surely it's a question of defense; surely it cannot be done without some encouragement from the government. Now for the first time this encouragement begins to be forthcoming.

The strength of our society is that each of us, in his own way, can make a contribution toward it. If a new building is built in a crowded area, you can put in a strong shelter in the basement which people in the building can reach in five or ten minutes, which has its own air supply, and which in all probability will survive. If somebody is considering putting up a nuclear reactor which has to have an enclosure to prevent escape of radioactive gases in case of an accident, he can put the whole reactor deep underground, in which case the reactor can survive a nuclear attack. We could persuade and make it possible for the owners and operators of gasoline stations to have ten times their present stockpile of gasoline to be contained in a place that can probably survive 10 p.s.i. over pressure. Then we could be fairly sure that the transportation system in the United States would not break down immediately. If anyone has an idea how he can make survival and recovery possible, I think any reasonable idea is likely to be met with at least some serious concern and possibly some help from the Department of Defense. I cannot tell you what to do, but I can say that the opportunity is here to do something.

Q. Dr. Teller, getting away from the sociological aspect of the future — In a lot of men's minds we're at dotting the *i*'s and crossing the *t*'s knowledge of the physical world. I know you don't think so, but a lot of people do. I wonder if you would like to express your ideas of where we might break through next.

A. I cannot. I have mentioned to you already the things that I feel are really interesting: a universal formulation of the laws of physics and understanding of life and consciousness or at least a better definition of the problem. In technology we can engineer materials now almost as effectively as we engineered bridges in the past. I I am sure that I have left out the most interesting things — but, as I say, I'm stupid.

Q. Could you tell us possibly how rapidly background radiation levels will decrease to the extent that a person could get out of his shelter and begin to take part in a life above ground? Let's take an area, say, fifty miles away from the major blast area or something like this?

A. How long do you have to stay in shelter I do not know. There will be many places — I think most places — where you probably need not go into shelter ever, or where you will have to be down there for maybe half an hour. There will be other places where you should remain in the shelter for maybe two weeks, and there may be places where it will be advisable to be under even longer. You will be able to come out for short periods, but you should not do so unnecessarily. If in the main attack the cities are ruined, you probably will not have any acceptable place to sleep in except the shelter. You will have to begin to rebuild everything else. I I believe that this question somehow misses the problem. The shelter as a place of reasonably reliable safety will remain and people will probably not be in a dreadful hurry to get out of it. But what is necessary will be to have a beginning of a purposeful activity.

Q. Basically, sir, my question was this: How long shall we plan to survive in these shelters?

A. The basic point is: It is rational, it is reasonable, to have in the shelters food supplies for two weeks. You may not need it and it may not be enough. Either can happen. If it is not enough you should be able to communicate with the rest of the world, and, if you need help in two weeks, in all probability help can come to you wherever you are.

Q. Can you conjecture what the reasons back of the hundred megaton bomb may be, what the Russian mind is working toward?

A. My Russian unfortunately is not quite functional. And I cannot read the Russian mind or Khrushchev. My conception of the hundred megatons is that it is the latest version of the shoe which is banging the table. There are very few military things which require a hundred megatons and, to the extent that a hundred megatons are required, you could easily do with a few five megaton bombs instead. The one thing is that you can probably deduce from the hundred megatons announcement is that this is probably not the purpose of the renewal of the tests. There is in the banging shoe some purpose, whether it is to try to frighten us, whether it is to hide the fact that they are trying out a new defense against our rockets. I can imagine many reasons and the hundred megatons is a most excellent propaganda device. It's so terrible that it deflects attention from all the essentials and does not in any way indicate which of many purposes is the real one.

Q. Dr. Teller, at recent conferences, particularly the Pugwash conferences, American scientists have been greatly impressed by the desire of the Russian scientific community to cease nuclear testing, disarm, and have peace. Do recent events imply that integrity has broken down in the scientific community; essentially, that the Russian scientists are hypocritical?

A. I don't know what to say. To my knowledge the Russian scientists do not happen to determine Russian politics. Also, I do not know how to take a statement that scientists or Russian scientists are hypocritical. In my opinion, all of us are honest and all of us are hypocritical. Sometimes the one, sometimes the other, sometimes a little more, sometimes a little less, and this holds for scientists, economists, lawyers, and football players. I don't think that there is a strict rule that any occupation is morally better than any other and every occupation tends to be excellent in its own field. If you would have told me that a certain group of scientists have made a demonstrably false and stupid statement about the solution of a differential equation, that would be a challenge for me. Then I would have to scratch my head and look for an explanation. But that the desires of a small group of Russian scientists do not precisely correspond with Nikita's actions, I don't think that this should be surprising to anybody. It can be explained by certain Russian scientists being hypocritical, by Russians allowing only certain scientists which have been selected for certain purposes to leave Russia. It might be true that all these scientists are perfectly honest and decent characters but Nikita doesn't happen to have told them what he intends to do next. There are so many explanations of your question that I am embarrassed to use any. I can only recommend that in the future less confidence, less decisions, should be based on the assumption that the desires of a small uninfluential group of people is indicative of what all Russia wants or Nikita will do, which again are two different things.

Q. Why do you interpret the resumption of testing by the Soviet as a sign of strength rather than as a sign of weakness?

A. I am making the unreasonable assumption that Nikita is reasonable. He has been rather shrewd in the past. You may assume that the Russians needed development of their nuclear weapons so badly that they were forced to test them. It's a very popular assumption; it has the incomparable merit that it is an agreeable assumpion. We like to believe it.

On the other hand, it has a slight flaw. If the Russians need testing so badly, why don't they do it secretly? It can be done easily. In fact, the most reasonable assumption for their present act is that they did test secretly. Three years of secret testing should have carried them way ahead of us. By now Khrushchev is so far ahead of us that he can shrug his shoulders and say: "Well, if the Americans want to run in this race, I don't care; I'm way ahead of them." If you assume that Khrushchev is realistic about the situation, I find it very hard to assume that he would behave in this challenging manner unless he really has quite a bit of strength to back it up. And the instruments to get the strength were at his hand all along. He could have tested and, if he had tested, then he would have gained the kind of strength which he now indicates that he has.

Q. Dr. Teller, how can we escape being behind the eight ball waiting for the other man to shoot first, if ever?

A. Well, let me tell you what I believe. I may be wrong, but this is what I honestly believe. I believe, in complete sincerity, that we must never shoot first. I don't think we want to do it; I don't think we ever will have the determination to do it; and I don't believe that we should ever have the determination to do it.

First of all, we need civilian defense, a recovery capability, an organization to recover after the attack. If we ever should happen to know that he is going to shoot tomorrow, we go underground. People go into their shelters and we will have to play the game from there. In actual fact, it would be a terrible thing, but by far not as terrible as the war. If we are forced to do this, it will put people into a psychological state where they will be willing to work very much harder, because everybody would realize that this is war. If Nikita's purpose is to keep us underground, he will have stimulated us into very purposeful activity. We need never strike first. We can make quite sure that most of our people will survive and that we can strike back and that the Russians will then be worse off than we are. Being a richer country, we shall be able to establish satisfactory stockpiles which will help us to recover.

By not striking first and being strong in our defense, we can prolong peace. If we can prolong peace and if we take imaginative steps toward world organization, we can exercise pressure on the Russians.

I do not believe in going back to Geneva and talking to them because they very obviously don't mean busines right now. Why should they? They have gone from victory to victory. We must stop their progress. We cannot do that unless we take our military preparation much more seriously. In ten years or twenty years we can put Russia under such pressure that by that time they will begin to give, in what direction and how I do not know. It is the next step; the first step is: we must stop the progress of communism through the world. I want to negotiate, but only after having stopped them first.

Q. What can we do about the problem of Red China?

A. I would like to have the privilege of answering this question and then to beg off. Red China is by several decades behind Russia.

They may test a nuclear explosive in a month for all I know. In fact, the Russian shots may have had the purpose of taking away publicity from Mao Te-Tsung. But, even if the Chinese tested a nuclear explosive, it would increase their value — I mean their nuisance value — immeasurably, but it would not make them really powerful. To be powerful, you must have a number of weapons and you must have a number of delivery vehicles. For all of these the Chinese will have to rely on Nikita.

I am not saying that China may not become dangerous in 1980 or 1990 or 2000. But, unless we do something about it, the United States will cease to exist in 1970. We do not want to worry about the real problem: how to stop the Russians. The problem is difficult. So we invent other problems. Like, for instance, how to fight fallout from tests, which is not dangerous at all. Or how to fight China, which is dangerous but by far not as dangerous. We have an excuse to think less about Russia. We may even imagine that Russia and China will fight each other and we don't need to worry.

Russia is a very great, a very acute, danger for our nation and for the free world. We will not survive unless we apply all our imagination, all our energy, all our determination, and all our willingness to cooperate with others, to cooperate with the Europeans, and maybe with Africans and South Americans and Asians. We must think in these terms and we must be willing to stop having a better standard of living and we must find means to channel our energy toward survival and toward the improvement of the rest of the world. If we are not willing to do those things, I think we will not live long enough to worry about China. If we do the right things in connection with Russia, then in ten years and in twenty years the world will have changed so completely we'll hardly recognize our own society. There will be plenty of time then to ask what to do about China.

China is a marvelous example of an unreal problem which is sufficiently close to being real so that it has deflected the eyes of many people from the real danger. But the real danger is there and the real danger is Communist Russia. And the real danger is to be faced, not by bombing Russia, but by being strong in all kinds of ways and thereby preventing the Russian attack. The Russian danger is to be faced by planning in a reasonable way, in our way where each individual makes his contribution, not merely to our society, but for our society and the rest of the world in which our society must live. This is the main thing.

Let me perhaps disregard your question or consider it as

answered and just add this: If I consider the history of the Industrial Revolution as unfinished, I will have to make the prediction that the Industrial Revolution will be completed in our century. That an industrial society will have been established certainly by 2050 and possibly even by 2000 throughout the world. This I think is very sure. Another thing is sure — that it will be coupled with the introduction of some world government. The uncertain thing is the little detail whether this will be on the Russian model or on our model. And this is the point on which our actions will have a decisive influence.

TOP MANAGEMENT GUIDES FOR
RESEARCH PLANNING

JAMES BRIAN QUINN

JAMES BRIAN QUINN

Associate Professor of Business Administration
Amos Tuck School of Business Administration
Dartmouth College
Hanover, New Hampshire

Professor Quinn received his B.S. in Engineering at Yale University, his M.B.A. degree from Harvard University Graduate School of Business Administration, and his Ph.D. from Columbia University. He served as an assistant head of Research Services, Allen B. DuMont Laboratories, then turned to teaching at the University of Connecticut and later at the Amos Tuck School of Business Administration of Dartmouth College.

Professor Quinn has just completed a major, two-year study of industrial research under a grant from the Alfred P. Sloan Foundation. This study was directed at the management and planning of research and development programs by corporations. As a result of a previous study supported by a grant from Arthur D. Little, Inc., Professor Quinn wrote the book, Yardstick of Industrial Research *(Ronald Press, 1959), and has produced many significant papers in the field of research planning and its relationship to long-range planning.*

Top Management Guides for Research Planning

What kind of guidance can and should top-level management provide in the planning of its research operations? Its most essential activities [1] in this sphere are:

(1) Establishing meaningful objectives for research.
(2) Seeing that the organization is attuned to the company's major long-term technological threats and opportunities.
(3) Developing an over-all business strategy into which research is integrated.
(4) Developing a procedure which evaluates research projects in light of company goals and capacities.
(5) Organizing research and operations for a maximum transfer of technology from research to operations.

This paper will analyze why each of these activities is critical, what problems each involves, and how these problems can best be overcome.

OBJECTIVE SETTING

As with any other aspect of industrial planning, research planning should begin with the establishment of the targets the activity is to shoot toward — over-all organizational objectives. But in most organizations there is great confusion over the nature and use of objectives in planning. What are objectives? Why

AUTHOR'S NOTE: This paper is based on a two-year study which included interviews with over 120 top research, operating, and planning executives in 35 major companies in the chemical, electrical, electronics, basic metals, and pharamceutical industries. The author gratefully acknowledges a research grant from the Alfred P. Sloan Foundation.

[1] These activities have been developed into an integrated research planning system in: James Brian Quinn, "Long-Range Planning of Industrial Research," *Harvard Business Review*, July-August 1961, substantial parts of which are reproduced herein by special permission of the publisher.

are they needed? How do they come into being? Where and why do failures occur in establishing objectives for research? These are common questions. If we can dispel some of the major misunderstandings about these issues, perhaps management can avoid one of the most common pitfalls in research planning — inadequate objective formulation.

What Are Objectives?

Objectives are targets or goals. They state the results that the organization or any of its components should accomplish. Objectives do not take just one form. They should exist at all levels in the organization in a definite hierarchy.

At the top of the pile are the relatively permanent "value objectives" of the total organization. These link together the value premises which should guide the organization's actions. They state the firm's desire for employee happiness, value of products, honesty to all, profits to stockholders, etc. These are selected by the owners or general management for the whole organization and generally express some distillation of the moral values of the times [although you can always have value objectives like those of the Al Capone organization which are rather individualistic]. While "value objectives" may well serve as guides for potentially errant managers, they are of relatively little use in planning.

But in business enterprises — immediately subordinate to the "value objectives" — there is a group of "over-all business objectives" which are critical to the planning process. These establish the intended nature of the specific business enterprise and the directions in which it should move. These over-all business objectives are somewhat less permanent than value objectives, but nevertheless usually stand for years. General management should, of course, establish these objectives because they are targets for all elements of the organization.

Below this level are a series of less permanent goals which define targets for each organizational unit, its subunits, and finally each activity within the subunit. The critical objectives here are those at the "over-all business objective" and the "organizational objective" levels. Formulation of both is a top management responsibility. Below this level top management's concern is just to see that those who establish goals keep them consistent with higher level objectives.

Why Define Objectives for Research?

There are three overwhelming reasons for setting clear objectives for research:

(1) Objectives provide the only usable criteria for judging the adequacy of research plans. If present (or proposed) programs will not propel the company to its goals, they must be replanned. For example:

> One large company set as its goal a 10% annual sales growth rate. Because of the company's size and the nature of its markets, antitrust laws foreclosed the possibility of acquisitions. Growth therefore had to be internally generated. Market planners thought that if present products were given adequate technological defense and were skillfully marketed, the company would achieve a 2% to 3% growth rate because of population factors. But research planners evaluated 85% of current R & D programs as essentially defensive. By a simple ratio analysis it became obvious that the company was in effect expecting each dollar of offensive R & D — i.e., the other 15% of its program — to yield approximately $25 per year of new product sales. To expect such a high impact ratio was entirely unrealistic. Consequently the company had to thoroughly reassess its offensive programs and its total program balance.

(2) Objectives allow self planning in creative organizations. They do not *constrain* action like other plans, i.e., policies, procedures, or methods. Properly established, objectives tell the organization *what* it is to accomplish, not *how* to do it. Creative persons are thus left free to select their own approaches to needed solutions.

(3) Objectives provide the only criteria by which actual research performance can be judged. On a national level we have an outstanding example of the confusion that is caused when this maxim is not followed.

> The U.S. missile program was conceived primarily to support goals of national defense and scientific investigation. Whether or not the decision was a good one, the program initially was not intended particularly to enhance the national image in the eyes of the world. The R & D program as drawn up and

executed appears to be successfully meeting the goals originally set for it. Hence it should be considered a success. But suddenly the goal of national publicity has been retroactively applied. The result is disillusionment and confusion.[2]

How Do Objectives Come Into Being?

Granted the need for objectives, how do they come into being in an organization? They can originate in three different ways: (a) by "enunciation," i.e., by management's carefully assessing the organization's future purposes and communicating these in an organized system; (b) by "appeal," i.e., by subordinate groups' submitting proposals to management until its pattern of decisions indicates that an organizational objective exists (even though not formally enunciated); (c) by "external imposition," i.e., by outside pressures such as the government, labor unions, or the international situation forcing the company in certain directions. In most complex organizations objectives originate by all three methods.

But consistent management decisions are the only way to keep an established objective in existence. Once decisions begin to contradict understood objectives, the organization cannot direct itself toward the goal with confidence. At this point the utility of the objective — no matter how clearly and how often enunciated — has ceased. Enough decisions consistently contradicting a given goal will eventually create a new goal. Until then confusion reigns. Consequently, all key decision makers must have a clear idea of the firm's objectives and back these with consistent decisions throughout the organization.

Key Problems in Establishing Objectives

Let us look at some of the major causes of failure in establishing objectives for research and some of the approaches specific companies have found useful in dealing with these problems. The most common failures can perhaps be classified as follows:

1. *Objectives change too often.* Managements allow "urgent competitive pressures" to dominate decisions. Hence the whole organization becomes oriented to the "profit now" objective

[2] This argument is developed in depth in R. E. Lapp, *Man and Space — The Next Decade*, New York, Harper and Brothers, 1961.

and overdiscounts — or ignores — future needs until they become crying present realities. Thus longer term fundamental and applied research either lack guidance altogether or are essentially converted into short-term service activities supporting current marketing or production goals.

2. *Objectives are distorted by the organization.* This problem can never be completely overcome. For each time an objective is transmitted from one person to another, the person receiving the transmission reinterprets the objective within his own framework. Thus small distortions introduced by somewhat inconsistent top-level viewpoints are likely to be amplified by each link in the chain of authorities transmitting the objective down into the organization. Researchers can only self-direct themselves meaningfully if these distortions are minimized by careful management action.

3. *Objectives are too general.* A most common problem where objectives are enunciated formally is to express them too vaguely for use as planning guides or criteria for judging action. Such over-generalized goals usually take the form of "value objectives." But too frequently even "over-all business objectives" are thought out in such vague terms as "growing as rapidly as possible," "diversification in any profitable direction," etc. While not imposing constraints on research, such objectives do not help stimulate research in desired directions.

4. *Objectives can be too specific.* Some organizationally immature operations overplan research by setting goals in too great detail. Such goals take either of two forms: (a) specific materials, pieces of hardware, test measurements, components, etc., demanded by operating groups, or (b) step-by-step experimental goals. Such goals occur when operating or staff groups dominate the research function. The obvious result is that research is constrained in its approaches to problems since it is told *how* to do the job, not *what* is to be done.

The experience of several companies may demonstrate some interesting ways of attacking these problems.

On the issue of the short-term orientation of decisions, the chairman of the board of one large concern said: "Any damn fool can make a profit for a month — or even a year — by gutting the organization's future. Top management's job is to keep the company 'future-oriented.' We try to do this by using a complex of *long-term* management controls. We play down the use of current profit and return standards in any rigid sense. And we purposely use intuitive judgments concerning how well each operating unit is building its organization and technology to meet future demands. So far we have resisted taking on board members from banks and financial houses because we think such people overemphasize current profits at the expense of future strength."

A pharmaceutical company reports that its president and chief technical executives visit the central laboratory once a month and talk with individual researchers about their work and evolving company goals and needs. The executives get to talk to each researcher about once a quarter. The company reports that the activity is a real stimulus to researchers because they feel management has a positive interest in their work and they genuinely understand company objectives.

A large company has both a centralized planning group and divisional planning groups. The central group reports to an Executive Committee, consisting of general corporate managers. Each year, to initiate the company's planning process, the Executive Commitee — with the help of Central Planning — draws up and circulates a statement of general corporate goals for the next five years. Targets for each division are included as a part of the statement. Before formal division planning begins, appropriate representatives of the Executive Committee personally discuss these targets with each division manager and his planning manager. Each division then draws up a set of plans — supported by budgets — to meet agreed upon goals. All plans are screened by the Central Planning group and then sent to a Long-Range Planning Committee (of the Executive Committee) for final coordination into the corporate plan. The corporate plan then becomes the basis for appraisal of budgets, and the division goals expressed within it become standards against which division performance is evaluated.

Types of Objectives Needed

Fortunately the kinds of objectives which are most vital to research planning can be established — with proper care — to avoid the pitfalls noted above. A later section on *The Research Mission* will describe the kinds of "organizational objectives" which should be considered for research. Formulation of these logically follows the forecasting of technological threats and opportunities and the establishment of a research strategy. The following examples will illustrate what "over-all business objectives" [3] are most critical to research planning and what issues these should resolve for maximum effectiveness:

The kinds of businesses the company wants to be in. These can be best expressed in terms of the kinds of markets the company will sell in and the functions its products must perform for customers. Thus an "electronics" company should consider whether it will be in the "communications" business, the "industrial controls" business, the "consumer appliance" business, the "quality laboratory measurements" business, etc. Each of these businesses requires a different kind of research backup in terms of program scope and balance. Obviously a broad based company will seek a position in several such businesses simultaneously. This simply means that it should be careful to back each with the research needed to accomplish its goals.

Method of growth intended. Is growth to be achieved by acquisition, merger, internal development, or a combination of approaches? Each approach carries different financial and organizational commitments and affects research program size and balance.

Direction of growth. Is the company to grow vertically toward markets or raw materials or horizontally into new areas at the same level of distribution? Should it find new fields or further penetrate present markets? Should the company be a broad-line producer or specialize in limited fields? Should it hedge cyclical products with countercyclical products, etc.? Such considerations obviously affect the internal balance of the research program tremendously.

Rate of growth. Recognizing the limits of its personnel, resources, and markets, how fast should the company reasonably hope to grow? What should the timing and pattern of such

[3] The author has amplified some of these in "Long-Range Planning of Industrial Research," op. cit.

growth be in each market area and over-all? This requires careful thought because too rapid growth can be as dangerous as too little growth. Unless all resources including technology are carefully built up to support a new market position, the company will be easy prey to a slower moving competitor with better developed backing for his product or service.

Allowable dependence on suppliers. Are the company's raw material markets stable or should alternative materials be sought? Is competition among vendors sufficient to insure technical progressiveness and low cost? Are individual vendors strong enough to support technical programs of their own or should these be supplemented? Management must decide how much of a risk it is willing to take on supplier relationships. A company can often gain some degree of control over its supply markets and individual suppliers by obtaining superior knowledge of the properties of purchased materials, processes for manufacturing purchased items, or possible substitute items. Again the company's goal of "independence of supply" affects research program scope and emphasis.

The kind of capital structure desired. (Particularly in smaller companies) the desired capital structure affects the length of time the company can wait for research payoffs, the amount of technology the company can exploit without damaging ownership goals, the degree of risk the company can assume on projects, etc. These, in turn, influence total program size and balance on long-term vs. short-term projects.

The degree of stability desired. Because of stock price considerations, ownership needs, banking relationships, etc., a given company may desire earning and sales stability as opposed to more rapid but risky growth. The degree of stability needed will affect the emphasis placed on more "sure fire" applied projects and smaller impact technology which may sacrifice potentially greater gains for lower risk.

Other business objectives. Other objectives commonly stimulate or restrict certain research programs. These include: the desired company image, its intended size, the allowable degree of government control, the percentage of market to be held in total and by geographical areas, the degree of technical flexibility desired, the price-volume and profit-volume markets the company wants to be in, the degree of decentralization intended, the company's desired size, and rate of return on investment.

Obviously initial decisions concerning objectives will be modi-fied as information from later planning stages becomes available. But orderly research planning must begin with a clear understand-ing of the directions the company wants to go and the confidence that these directions will not be constantly changing. Without such guidance the program will inevitably drift toward studies that fascinate individual scientists, toward pet projects of key executives, or toward sales service — or similar short-run activi-ties — which bear little relationship to long-term company needs.

Determining Technological Threats and Opportunities

Research must be responsive to technological flows from three sources: the *scientific community* generally, the company's pres-ent and potential *customers,* and the company's *competitors.*

Let us see what is involved in assessing the threats and oppor-tunities offered by each of these three flows. Since other papers at this Conference discuss elements of how such technological forecasts are made, I shall concentrate on the top management questions they raise: What kinds of organizations have been found useful for forecasting technology? What kinds of infor-mation should management expect forecasters to consider and to provide the planning process? And what kinds of problems are encountered in forecasting technological threats and oppor-tunities?

Concepts of Technological Forecasting

The first thing to emphasize is that forecasting is *not* planning. Forecasts assess future environments and the mutual impact of these environments on the company and the company on the environments. Planning occurs later when management takes forecast information and converts it into goals, policies, programs, and procedures which guide action. Forecasting can be delegated to staff groups. Planning from the forecasts should always be a line of activity. Planning requires that action decisions be made and followed up with authority delegations, assignments of re-sponsibilities, and controls to see that these assignments are car-ried out. This is where many "planning programs" fail. Staff planning groups anticipate problems or foresee opportunities. They evaluate alternatives and even recommend action in reports which are carefully "accepted" by management. But then nothing happens. Line managers continue to make decisions as if the staff group's analysis — and the problems and opportunities themselves — never existed. Top management thus should see that technological forecasts are used for decision making or else not waste money on them.

Another important point. Management is interested in forecast accuracy, not precision. No one can forecast the precise technologies which will be needed and available three to seven years ahead. Yet management decisions on staffing new knowledge areas, planning exploitation of present research results, making major organizational changes, and so on, demand such lead times. Fortunately, what such decisions require is information about the *direction* future technology is likely to take and the *probable ranges* of technologies which might be faced. As the future unfolds, early long-range decisions can be modified, nullified, or reinforced — provided sufficient flexibility has been built into initial plans. Forecasters can be expected to provide accurate enough range forecast information for these early plans to propel the company in proper directions.

Finally, unlike other areas of forecasting, mathematical formulations are almost worthless in technological forecasting. The requisites are human judgment, a knowledge of the scientific field under study, a real sense of the economic implications of science, and imagination without stargazing. To be effective each phase of such forecasting must be the specific responsibility of some competent individual or organization. Let us see what kinds of approaches have been used in evaluating each of the three technological flows affecting research.

The General Scientific Environment and Competitive Technology

Forecasts of the general scientific environment — and the impact of competitive science in particular — may take several possible forms. The following examples offer an excellent overview of major approaches:

Some companies have developed grids[4] of all the basic sciences which might potentially impinge on their operations. On a preset schedule they review each scientific field on two bases. First they investigate whether the science: (a) is beginning to show promise of breakthroughs, (b) is highly active with major contributions being made rapidly, (c) is slowly approaching saturation, or (d) is scientifically dormant. Second, they evaluate whether the science is developing in directions which appear to be more (or less) closely associated with the company's long-term goals. These two parameters help determine whether a given field needs increased or decreased emphasis in the company's fundamental program. Such reviews are made by the company's most competent available scientist(s) in each field with such outside support as the company may feel is warranted.

Other companies select for study specific knowledge areas which researchers or executives think might eventually impinge on their company's operations. Staff groups then assess the scientific potential of these individual fields and their potential economic implications if certain solutions are found. An individual study could take several man-months and usually involves an investigation of the "state of the art," important knowledge gaps, the current work being done, the magnitude of the field's potential economic impact, and the availability of qualified personnel to man the field.

Many studies — both within and without industry — have projected the future state of the art in various technological fields. These have attempted to estimate what technology will be needed and available in such end-use fields as computers, automatic production devices, transportation, space, communications, energy, etc.[5] The technique most commonly used in such studies is to forecast critical sociological factors whose change will create a certain set of demands for technology.

[4] One such check list is provided by the Specialties List of the National Register of Scientific and Technical Personnel.

[5] Published examples include: Ralph E. Lapp, *Man and Space — The Next Decade*, New York, Harper and Brothers, 1961. Harrison Brown, *Challenge of Man's Future*, New York, Viking Press, 1954. Hans Thirring, *Energy for Man*, Bloomington, Indiana University Press, 1958.

Present technology is compared against these needs and gaps are noted. The forecaster then identifies the missing key facts which compose these gaps. Present fundamental and applied programs indicate which of these problems are being worked on and with what seeming progress. Past experience with similar problems provides a basis for determining probability of success and the potential timing of solutions. Then by cataloging significant breakthroughs and trends, the forecaster can extrapolate developing knowledge into the future and estimate the future technical configuration of the field under study.

Many companies evaluate competitive technology both formally and informally. In fundamental research liberal publication policies and free informal exchanges make it relatively easy to evaluate the scope of competitors' programs. Many research directors say they know to a man who is working on what in competitors' fundamental research. Several companies keep accurate tabulations of publications and patents by competitors and break them down into knowledge areas to assess competitive progress in critical spheres. Many companies make annual product comparisons to identify where their products are superior or need defensive support.[6]

Forecasts of the scientific environment are typically provided by one of three organizational devices: (1) a staff analysis group, (2) a research committee, or (3) an *ad hoc* special study group. Each approach presents its special advantages and problems. Two interesting combination approaches illustrate solutions some companies have found useful.

Several research directors indicated success in having research scientists assist a respected staff group in preparing forecasts. They say this approach both utilizes the special skills and information sources the staff group has and forces the researchers involved to think rigorously about the potential of their scientific fields and their contributions to it.

The vice president of research in one electronics company annually assigns a team of newly hired Ph.D.'s to study the potential impact of their own scientific specialties. As new

[6] Several systems for doing this are found in J. B. Quinn, *Yardsticks for Industrial Research*, New York, Ronald Press, 1959.

personnel they are not influenced by past company biases. Their report goes directly to the research committee.

Customer Needs

Of all possible technology flows, the company is most interested in those which impinge on the needs of its present and potential customers. Projecting technology to support present lines is not uncommon. As a matter of routine some market research groups look ahead to customer needs three to five years in the future. But too often market research groups get bogged down in problems of the present. Some of the more sophisticated *organizational devices* to insure a longer term orientation to the needs of present and potential customers include the following:

A chemical company invites is customers' technical and management personnel to seminars at which they discuss their developing scientific problems and learn about the sponsor's own current research programs. The company then tries to meet defined needs through its own R & D program and through cooperative research with customers.

A T & T has long supported a sizable systems-engineering group which (on the basis of demographic data, call information, system problems, anticipated new means of communication, and so on) expresses needed future technology in terms of "black boxes" (of known performance characteristics) to be developed by R & D. The group must constantly look far enough into the future to keep adopted technology from creating system-wide bottlenecks 10 to 20 years ahead.

One company has a long-range marketing research group of technical people whose sole responsibility is to contact those charged with long-range thinking in customer and potential customer companies. On the basis of this information they try to meet future technical needs — three to ten years ahead. The group claims to be able to spot needs and opportunities that customers themselves cannot see because of operating biases and the fact that they are constantly putting out technological "brush fires."

Some specific *techniques* used in identifying areas where longer term research could propel the company into new or expanded markets are also interesting:

A glass company considers those properties of its product (glass) which are unique unto it, i.e., exceptional tensile strength, chemical resistance, translucency, ductility, etc. It then seeks to identify present and potential markets in which consideration of one or more such properties is a dominant factor. Its applied research program then seeks glasses with intensified properties needed to meet recognized market needs. Its fundamental program seeks primarily to further isolate and understand the properties of various glasses.

A basic metals company by extensive field research seeks to identify those applications where its products can most nearly be substituted for the dominant competing product. It then identifies the performance limits which preclude its present product's entry into the desired market. Where economically feasible, applied research works on the improvement of these performance limits. Fundamental research investigates the phenomena limiting the performance of the metal's compounds and alloys.

A chemical company seeks what it calls "the critical operating characteristic" of each of its major products. This is the characteristic which — if improved slightly — will most dramatically influence product sales. This becomes the focal point for applied research. For most products the nature of this critical characteristic is said to remain stable over a moderate — 2- to 5-year — period.

Such market research guidance helps stimulate long-range research in useful directions but does not constrain scientific approaches by overdetailing the specifications of needed products.

Top Management Considerations

Obviously, top management does not need to be involved in the details of technological forecasting. But it should expect research planning to be based upon adequate forecast data and to see that proper organizational devices exist to provide it. These organizations must look far enough ahead to allow research planning adequate lead time and not be overly biased by short-term considerations or by traditional ways of attacking problems. The effects of the latter kind of bias can be tragic. For example:

In a large chemical company a product area had been disregarded as "too small relative to our operation" to be worth the company's while. A brief discussion established the fact that if certain solutions could be found, the product had an annual potential of $10 billion. This sounds fantastic, but the company had only considered the traditional way of doing things in the market under consideration. It had not thought about what chemistry could do to change the field totally.

Significantly, the *most profitable opportunities* and the *most serious threats* offered by technology frequently come from looking at old problems in entirely new ways — not from traditional approaches gently mutating accepted technology. As examples:

The indigo industry was subverted not by traditional dye sources, but by the development of synthetic dyes through chemistry. Polymer research — not agricultural research — recently transformed the textile field and the rubber business. Solid state physics is revolutionizing electronics. Plastics are on their way toward transforming the housing, packaging, and metals fields. The accidental discovery of penicillin brought a whole new approach to the attack on certain medical problems. Psychology has recently made dramatic advances — not because of traditional therapeutic techniques — but because of chemistry.

Finally, technological forecasting must take a broad enough viewpoint to insure that research planners recognize the opportunities and threats posed by change in the general economic and sociological environment. This means that they must consider trends in economic conditions, the demographic structure, shifting expenditure priorities, the role of government in the economy, public and legal attitudes toward business, international affairs, future labor conditions, and so on. Analyses of such factors have led particular companies to research policies which more limited commercial considerations would not have dictated. For example:

Some companies are beginning to orient some of their technological thinking toward arms control. This move is based on a changing U.S. and international attitude toward such activities, as well as the growing potential of a multibillion-dollar business in arms control devices.

Demographic analyses have shown the need for research into many fields: geriatrics, nonfossil energy sources, synthetic foods, recovery of water and chemicals from the sea and air, water purification, sewage disposal, traffic control, exotic sources of food and raw materials, and chemical means for contraception — to name only a few.

Recognizing potential public and legal pressures, some companies have established broad fundamental research programs and even entire laboratories for the primary purpose of producing technology for the public good. Others take on certain defense or health contracts — outside their normal spheres of interest — on a nominal (or non-) profit basis and contribute resulting knowledge to the public domain. Some companies restrict research and growth which would apply to areas that might create cries of "giantism" or "stifling competition." Many freely exchange basic technology with competitors although this induces a higher degree of competition in markets they could otherwise dominate.

STRATEGY FOR RESEARCH

The next major top management consideration in research planning is to develop the over-all business strategy which research is to help support. An initial problem here is that the concept of strategy itself is so often misunderstood.

A strategy is a plan so complete that it takes into account possible countermoves of opposition groups. A strategy is an *implementing* plan. It supports an objective — or set of objectives — by determining *how* the organization can best achieve its desired ends in light of competitive (or other) opposing pressures and its own limited resources. Every competitive organization which survives in the long run must be stronger in some respects than its competitors. Conversely its competitors must exceed its strength in certain areas or else they would not survive.[7] The

---

[7] Of course, if either party is nurtured by a benevolent third party — such as the Government or Fate — it can have no comparative strengths and survive.

essence of strategic planning then is to marshal the organization's resources so that its comparative strengths are emphasized and the opposition's comparative strengths have the least negative effect on the organization.

This means, in research, that no company can be pre-eminent in all technological fields. Because of limited resources, each company must expose itself to some risks and pass up some opportunities. The research strategy problem is to establish — in light of expected competitive action — where the compny should: (a) concentrate its research efforts, (b) remain "on the grapevine" (in touch) with the scientific community, or (c) virtually ignore developing technology. Each company's peculiar strengths, weaknesses, and objectives will determine its optimum strategy. Let us look at the typical considerations in research strategy.

Major Research Programs

First, the company must minimize serious technological threats to its existence. As a starting point, it looks at positions which must be defended at all costs. Then it saturates these areas with research. Almost every company has a few lines or processes which are its "bread and butter." These must be defended with strong research commitments until design maturity eliminates returns from research or the company decides to phase out the products or processes themselves. Carefully forecasting customers' technological needs and watching competitive programs will indicate areas which need heavy developmental and applied research support. Cataloguing the limits of knowledge supporting these areas helps to delineate fields for strong *longer-range* research efforts.

For example, one large, limited-line, electronics equipment manufacturer said:

"Our company got into fundamental research because things were becoming too complicated to continue without it. We needed to know the physical limits of certain kinds of matter in order to develop machinery which could operate at increasingly high speeds and with increasing complexity. Purchase of our kind of equipment is a straight technical decision. The fastest, most reliable equipment for a job will sell. No other will. Consequently, whoever first obtains the basic knowledge in our field will dominate it. And we cannot afford to lose our present number one position. As a result, 80% of our fundamental program is now on composition of matter problems which we think pertain to our one primary equipment line. We try to exceed competitors' talent commitments in all these problem areas."

Next, the strategic plan outlines areas where optimum technological opportunities exist. Top management must determine these by a critical analysis of the company's particular strengths and weaknesses. Examples from the chemical industry illustrate three completely different strategies in actual companies:

Company A tries to make itself indispensable to its customers by high performance of its chemicals and special services. The company refuses to make chemicals which may face fierce price competition. The company makes only high-margin specialties whose volume is too small to interest the industry's giants. It sells mostly to small companies who tend to regard *Company A* as their own research department. To do this *Company A* must keep intimately in touch with its customers' needs and be a research leader in a few scientific fields tailored specifically to these needs. The company backs up its carefully restricted research program with a team of engineers highly specialized in flexible small plant operations.

Company B only enters fields requiring the complex technical skills it already has and/or raw materials to which it has special access. Its real strength lies in exploiting highly competitive situations by applying offbeat process technology. Consequently the company plans to grow only in fields with large, long-run volume potentials, not in those having short-term, high-margin potential and high technological obsolescence. The company backs up its strategy with a strong raw materials and process-oriented research commitment. It attempts to expand its range of technical skills slowly, but develops great depth in each skill it takes on.

Company C combines research with an acquisition strategy. After World War II, the parent company found itself with large amounts of cash, but with heavy investments in overseas resources and low-margin cyclical products and services. The company decided to diversify into the chemical field by acquisition. After several successful acquisitions made on a somewhat random basis, the company found itself with successful operations at both ends of the chemical spectrum — chemical specialties and heavy chemicals. But to fill out its line and provide profit stability, it needed intermediate-range — medium volume and margin — chemicals. With this as a target *Company C* started a long-range research program to provide: (a) the know-how to back up acquisitions of desirable small companies in these fields and (b) new intermediate-range chemicals on which to build a new division of its own.

Such considerations determine where a company's program should be strongest. Here the company must exceed competitors' talent commitments — not necessarily their dollar commitments — area by area.

Grapevine Programs

The strategic plan must also ensure: (a) that sudden advances in certain areas of science will not catch the company unaware and completely demolish a major segment of its business, and (b) that the company does not overlook exceptional exploitation opportunities offered by rapid developments in new scientific areas. Such is the function of "on the grapevine" or "connecting" programs. These programs keep the company aware of impinging technology so that, as major advances occur, it can move rapidly to (a) force competitors to cross-license otherwise damaging technology, or (b) develop market positions for itself and, at the same time, avoid preemption by competitors.

Research groups in each "connecting" area tend to be small. But they must be staffed with first-rate men who can be on the informal grapevine that exchanges scientific information freely. These men must make contributions themselves, and the company must allow them maximum freedom to publish and to participate in scientific meetings. Two examples will show how this element of strategy is implemented in practice:

One large company considers its laboratory a "window on the world." The laboratory's primary function is "to be in the main stream of pertinent science in order to be able to appreciate the implications of new science as it becomes available."

This means that the company can initiate crash programs in time to avert developing technological threats and can move rapidly to use new technology which is relevant to its operation. To be in the main stream of science, the company feels its laboratory must contribute "a fair share" to fundamental knowledge in all areas which might impinge on its operations. It therefore makes sure its program scope includes all active related sciences. And the company liberally encourages its researchers to publish their own scientific contributions.

A large chemical company uses a planning technique it calls the "limit forecast." In effect, it annually surveys all pertinent scientific fields and plans its program so that it can never take more than five years to catch up with major new technology hitting its field from any unconventional source. Such planning is possible because of (a) the company's own substantial financial capacities, (b) inertia in its markets and (c) long lead times in the industry caused by sizable investment requirements. The company feels that a five-year crash development program could put it into a good position to deal with any major threat either through cross-licensing or direct competition.

Problems in Strategic Planning

While the above concepts are straightforward, strategic planning is fraught with hazards. Let us look at the more common and significant problems in strategic planning for research.

The first big problem is determining objectively the critical strengths or weaknesses of the company. Two approaches are provocative:

A medium-sized electronics company made a study of the relative *market penetration* of its various products. The products with high penetration and profit return were considered successful. Those with low penetration *or* low profit return were considered unsuccessful. Top management tried to assess what factors had contributed most to the success of "successful lines." It also analyzed what factors had caused the failure of "unsuccessful" lines. It then tried to assess why the leading competitor was most successful in each area where the company had failed. The study indicated that the company's strengths lay in designing special components for precision jobs and selling such items direct. Its weaknesses were in competing in mass markets where low cost and advertising "pull" techniques were important. It then started a program to "spin off" the latter activities and to retrench into specialized markets backed by a fast moving engineering group and pilot scale plants.

A coal company used an *investment analysis* approach. It found that its investments were almost exclusively underground. Because of the technological maturity of the field, management felt further investments in the highly competitive underground operations would offer limited returns. It decided to do research which would yield above ground investment opportunities leading to special market positions. With this broad goal its research was most successful.

Unless a company adequately assesses its particular strengths and weaknesses and develops its resources properly around these, it will eventually be a "me too" operation, unsatisfactorily trying simply to meet competition on all fronts.

A second major problem: many managements do not recognize that — in organizing the company's resources — a "growth through research" strategy must be backed by entirely different kinds of financial and organizational commitments from more conventional market development or acquisition strategies. The research approach requires: (1) that management think in terms of a 5- to 7-year payback period instead of the 2- to 4-year period common to other investments, (2) that management be willing to make research investments with less certain information and a potentially higher risk than normal operating investments, (3) that a flexible long-term capital plan be developed to meet the unpredictable investment spurts and long investment cycles characteristic of research, (4) that operating departments be more technically oriented and highly coordinated to achieve maximum benefit from research technology, and (5) that the over-all organization to be planned to grow flexibly from within rather than through acquisition of entire experienced operating units from outside. Lack of such long-term thinking has often caused research failure in companies dominated by "merchant" or "financial" management whose approach is geared to near-term profit considerations.

Finally, strategic thinking is frequently biased by "the way things have always been done." This leads to problems like the following:

(1) Many companies tend to balance their R & D programs to match present product lines' sales or investment patterns rather than building programs to meet maximum technological threats and to take advantage of greatest technological opportunities.

(2) Few companies tend to balance their investment risks by purposely taking on extremely high risk projects a certain percentage of the time. Instead they tend to research traditional products on traditional sets of components and fail to look for really offbeat approaches which could upset the whole field. Although scientists themselves frequently would like to take a broader range of risks, they are often constrained by management's attempting to hold research to too detailed a profit contribution standard over too short a time base. Conversely, by limiting the scope of their research, these companies are simultaneously (and often unwittingly) exposing themselves to the threat that an entirely new technological approach taken by an outsider could completely upset their traditional market positions.

(3) Few companies have defined their research strategies broadly enough to defend themselves adequately against the eventual costs of "gadget changing and molecule manipulation" short-term technical orientations. Business is the institution our society has established to take its risks. In fact the only logical justification for "big business" besides economics of scale — and these are surpassed as soon as a company decentralizes — is to take risks other economic units cannot. Perhaps the paramount element of risk taking today is in scientific and technological spheres. Yet — despite a significant change in attitude in recent years — too few companies have really faced up to supporting the truly long-term research which is needed to keep U.S. industry in the technological forefront. Instead much of such research is still forced onto Institutes, the Federal Government, and educational institutions. In the long run, this exposes business to several extremely unpleasant possibilities:

(a) Specific industries can be more easily attacked by public groups with the eventual goal of greater public control over the businesses' operations. For example: the pharmaceutical industry today would undoubtedly be less prone to attack and eventual regulation if it could point to significant fundamental research contributions as justifying high margins and returns. Despite truly impressive developmental accomplishments, the industry does not enjoy as favorable a scientific image as it easily could in the eyes of the public or the medical profession.

(b) The groups supporting longer term research will eventually control large areas of basic knowledge and can make business subject to royalty payments and/or specific controls if it uses such knowledge. Atomic energy is a case in point.

(c) The government itself has another wedge to use in entering open productive competition with private enterprise. It has already entered the power producing field (not by this route however) and now has powerful technological entrees into the air transportation and satellite communications fields should it choose to use them.

(d) The total long-term research done in the U.S. may not be adequate. The result can only be that eventually certain foreign countries will usurp desirable markets which would otherwise belong to U.S. businesses.

(e) Even in considering U.S. markets many companies tend to overlook or discount rapidly developing *institutional* markets and the potential of new *public* consumption areas.

Such threats may in the long run be among the most serious of all strategic considerations for business.

Top management must overcome these serious difficulties and develop a broad research strategy which minimizes technological threats from present and potential competitors yet maximizes the company's own potential gains from the use of technology.

The Research Mission

The research organization can support any given strategy in a variety of ways. And it is up to top management to specify which types of support it expects from research. Is research to be the dominant source of new product and process ideas, or is this the function of sales or operating managers? To what extent should research simply service present products and processes? Is research to be the technological arm of management consulting on all aspects of the company's technological situation? Or should research be just a highly skilled pool of technical special-ists available to answer problems beyond the talents of divisional personnel? To what extent is research to support itself through patent income? Is research to provide a scientific "intelligence service" to keep the company aware of impinging technological threats or opportunities outside the sphere of traditional opera-tions? To what extent is research technology to be the basis of new product growth, new processes, or a general technological reputation for the company? Answers to such questions are crucial in designing a research program which best fits the company's needs.

By not defining the research mission carefully, many manage-ments, in effect, set research adrift without specific responsibili-ties in the over-all organization. Like any other organization, research can and must be held accountable (over a suitable period of time) for acomplishment of a particular portion of the com-pany's goals.[8] *Proper definition of corporate goals, strategies, and the research mission provide a firm basis by which manage-ment can hold the research organization responsible for specific accomplishments. Yet, if properly developed, these plans do not constrain the scientific approaches research uses in carrying out its mission.*

Project Selection

Next top management must be sure that it has a project selec-tion procedure which fits research into company goals. The process, of course, is exceedingly complex and requires much intuitive judgment, but project selection for an integrated re-search program essentially follows a three-step sequence: plan-ning technology (1) for present products, (2) for foreseeable new products, and (3) for entirely new applications.

Present Products

The process begins by assessing the technology needed to sup-port present lines two to ten years in the future. The first step is prediction of the company's potential market for each product class. Partly, this involves assessing what technology will keep the products attractive to customers despite inroads of substitute

[8] See James Brian Quinn, *Yardsticks for Industrial Research*, New York, Ronald Press, 1959.

items, competitive technology, and changing customer needs. Customers' technical needs and potential competitive technology are defined by the technological forecasting techniques already noted.

Planners then compare present technology with needed technology and identify gaps. If enough key facts are available to fill these gaps, defensive development or applied programs can be introduced (or continued) to fulfill established needs in the shortest possible time (usually within two to five years) and with a high probability of success. But if key facts are missing, the company will have to undertake "support" studies in the specific disciplines underlying needed technology.

Because scientific areas within which these studies are needed can often be rather clearly defined, their probability of technical success is usually reasonably high. Average lead times often lengthen to three to seven years if support studies are introduced. But past experience in the specific scientific areas supporting the product should be used as the guide to expected lead times and the number of people needed to staff each area. Regardless of whether the developmental or the combined developmental-support-fundamental approach is used, planned technology for existing lines proceeds from recognized needs to specific programs.

New Products

In a dynamic technological environment, however, present products — plus planned acquisitions — are unlikely to fulfill all company goals (see Figure 1). The next step is to find new market applications for present or new technology and then (through the forecasts noted) identify the specific technology needed to fulfill these applications. The needed technology is again matched against present technology and gaps noted. As before, the gaps can be attacked by either of two methods — "support" research or development. Before making substantial commitments to either approach the company should make exploratory investigations to determine the technical feasibilities of the various possible courses that are open to it.

As in the case of present products, if exploratory work indicates that enough key facts are known, development and applied programs can be undertaken with a high probability of success and a probable impact within two to five years. If key facts are

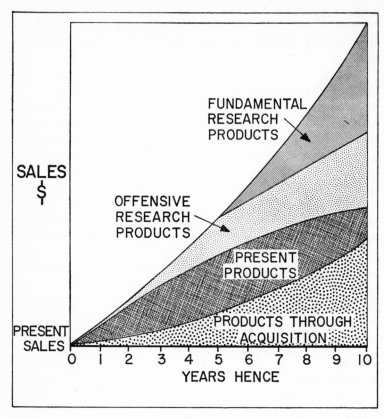

Figure 1

missing, support programs in defined areas can be initiated. Again, experience indicates the general probability of success and lead-time pattern in any given area, and specific project sizes are based on this estimate. These factors are typically determined by intuitive judgments. Only when research has reached quite applied stages are mathematical projections at all useful. But even in applied work, experience indicates that, while time schedules can be met by massing personnel on projects, budget estimates are only accurate within broad ranges.

Again, note that planning new lines first identifies market needs and then works back to sequential programs to meet these needs. Thus, optimum levels for both present and new product support are best developed by aggressively (a) seeking specific market needs, and (b) analyzing past experience in technological support areas to obtain the best possible estimates of success probabilities and project cost.

Fundamental Research

Addition of the offensive program still may not enable the company to meet its goals (see Figure 1 again). The company may need technology which develops entirely new applications beyond the scope of those presently foreseen. The company then needs a "fountainhead" fundamental research program. Here the planning process is reversed. First, technical planners must identify scientific areas which may provide the foundations for commercial end products compatible with company goals. Within these fields management should support specific project inquiries based on:

1. The rapidity with which technical advances are occurring.
2. The competence and enthusiasm of company personnel in the particular field.
3. The availability of qualified persons to staff scientific areas new to the company.
4. The anticipated amount of information yet to be discovered in an area.
5. The relative pertinence of the area's knowledge to company goals.

There is no alternative to an element of faith in planning fundamental research. Here the probability of a given project's leading to a commercial end product is low or unknown. Either it will yield "commercializable" technology or it will not. However, a rather stable percentage of the projects undertaken in a given field will frequently have commercial implications. Several companies with mature fundamental programs made statements like the following:

> "We can predict with some accuracy that we will have one major new capital-absorbing development as a result of fundamental research in that area next year. We don't know what the development will be; we do know we can expect it."

Despite the fact that many companies have analyzed their experiences over a long period of time and have come up with ratios showing so many dollars of sales (fixed investment or profits) per dollar of research, I know of no company which has found enough reliability in such ratios to use them rigorously for planning specific fundamental programs. Nevertheless, intuitive, "order of magnitude" judgments of these relationships, *scientific field by scientific field,* must — and do — underlie all determinations of whether the company has enough fundamental research to meet its goals. Management should, of course, bring to bear any data which may help reveal possible trouble spots in the fundamental program. But it should avoid using any figures rigidly. Ultimate decisions on this element of program balance must be left to trained scientists in whom management has confidence.

Detailed fundamental research planning indeed occurs from the "bottom up." Each researcher should be encouraged to select his own specific inquiries within his scientific specialty. Since these researchers should know more about their specialties than anyone else in the company, management's primary control is to make sure that their judgments are tempered by those of competent scientific executives who understand company goals and needs.

A large chemical company stated how its management gives the researcher maximum scope in selecting inquiries, yet does not lose control of this critical planning process:

"We expect the individual researcher to come up with project proposals within the area of his specialty. He discusses any new idea with his director. If the director is enthusiastic, he suggests that the researcher make a literature search, perform exploratory investigations, and report back in one month. If at the end of the month the area looks promising to the researcher and a small committee of research directors, the researcher is allowed to go ahead for another three months. His progress — and the promise of the field — is then checked again. If things are encouraging, he is given a commitment for six more months' work. The six-month review is the last informal review. If the project continues, it is thereafter reviewed annually by the Research Committee in the appropriate budget review cycle."

Other Technology

Although fitting projects into goals has been described in terms of sales and/or profit goals and present or new product lines, similar approaches are used to fit other technology into company goals. If specific needed technology can be defined, the program develops from the desired result back to the specific research project. If specific technology cannot be defined, the company plays the probabilities that fundamental research in broad scientific areas will produce applicable technology. These concepts apply whether the technology is for new processes, new raw-material sources, greater human safety, improved product quality, information for the public good, or any other of research's many possible outgrowths. The important factor is to work *from* company goals *to* a balanced research program that will meet these goals.

Program Balance

The final stage of project selection is balancing the final package of projects to meet company goals and strategies. So many detailed decisions are involved in the planning process that intended final program balance may be lost if management does not step back and take a careful overview of its final program. It must see that emphasis is balanced among:

Phases of effort — By seeing that long- and short-term goals are supported by adequate fundamental versus applied versus developmental research. More fundamental stages must feed new scientific possibilities to later stages and must find principles which are bottlenecking more applied programs. Applied and developmental programs should provide concrete evidence of research payoff in the near future.

Offensive versus defensive research — By making sure that the company is giving adequate attention to growth goals versus maintaining present businesses. This breakdown applies only to applied and developmental phases because earlier phases cannot be identified as to results sought.

Product lines supported — By subdividing applied and developmental programs to see whether each present and potential product line is getting sufficient offensive and defensive support to fulfill its particular subgoals.

Operating divisions supported — By seeing that each division's needs receive adequate attention when divisions and product lines do not coincide (as in the refining, distributing, transporting, and producing of oil).

Scientific areas — By ensuring, particularly in fundamental phases, that program scope includes all scientific fields presenting major long-range scientific threats or opportunities within the company's sphere of activity.

Types of results sought — By supporting goals with the proper levels of product technology, process technology, raw materials technology, public good technology, pursuit of general scientific understanding, and so forth.

No mathematical techniques can tell managers what the "right" balance is for their program. What is right for one company is wrong for another. The proper balance for any particular company depends solely on its goals, capacities, and strategies. These must be determined by seasoned management judgments. But this balance must not be regarded as a rigid cast. As certain project areas begin to produce results, they should receive added emphasis. Others become less attractive and must be deemphasized. The result is a constant dynamic rebalancing as the program progresses. In fact, one sure sign of program weakness is a static balance of emphasis over a long period.

RESEARCH TO OPERATIONS

One more crucial area for top-management advanced planning is in facilitating the transfer of technology from research to operations. Two sets of biases tend to restrict this transfer. On one hand is the researcher who often either does not recognize the commercial implications of his work or will not release his work until he has covered all of its possible scientific ramifications. On the other hand, operating groups often term research technology "impractical" because it was "invented by people who don't understand operating problems."

Perhaps the most insidious restriction appears when operating managers — many of whom are held to profit or return-on-investment standards — resist taking on research ideas which will add marketing or engineering development costs to their operations in the short run — despite the long-run desirability of such ideas.

Involving operating personnel in program planning and reviews tends to enhance their understanding of research progress and prepares the way for transfer of research technology to operations. Beyond this approach and the usual exchange of reports, individual companies have found the following organizational devices useful:

A large chemical company has formed a development division which it refers to as a "large flexible plumbing and cooking establishment." The development director is held to a profit responsibility. He makes his profit by pilot-plant production and sale of new products conceived in research. As soon as a product or process is successful in development, the appropriate operating division can request that the product be transferred to it. The development director has to try to pull other research ideas up to commercialization as soon as possible to continue making a profit. Consequently, there is a positive impetus to get ideas out of research, and operating managers do not resist taking on proven profitable ideas.

A pharmaceutical company pays the researcher a percentage of profits on any idea commercialized and encourages him to follow the product or process through to commercialization, if he has the talent and interest. In effect, the company sets up a small new profit center and operating division for each new product. The researcher thus has an interest in pushing his ideas, and there are no operating managers to resist taking on new products or processes.

By simple accounting entries a steel company segregates the "debugging" or "market introduction" costs of a new operation and puts them into a separate pool which is not charged directly to any operating division. These costs are only amortized to the specific operation after it has had sufficient time to get established.

A large electronics company emphasizes that the managers of its decentralized operating divisions are not held to a short-term profit standard, but are held to a complex of standards, an important one of which is "technical progressiveness." Management judges technical progressiveness by comparing each division's actual use of research technology against an estimate of how much research-produced technology *could have been* used by the division — the standards being, of course, subjective.

Such devices assist the transfer of technology from research to operations. But they are not total solutions in themselves. Optimum transfer of research technology to operations will occur only when research is properly integrated into the company's over-all plans by the kind of top management coordination outlined above.

SUMMARY

Top management's function in research planning thus is:

(1) To provide research with a clear understanding of company goals and strategies and to define a specific mission for research within the context of these plans.

(2) To see that appropriate organizational arrangements are made:
   a. To carefully assess the major technological threats and opportunities the company faces,
   b. To facilitate transfer of research technology into operations.

(3) To develop a project evaluation procedure which results in a balanced package of projects to meet company objectives.

From this point on management must continuously evaluate its program to see that both research and operating units carry out their intended functions in developing and utilizing technology to support company goals.

Q. You described one firm's procedure of having the researcher present his proposals to the director of research, of making the researcher do exploratory work and report in a month; then sending this to a screening committee; and so on through to an annual budget. Surely this procedure kills exploratory research?

A. No! This is a very successful research operation. The secret is that the entire company is highly science- and technical-oriented. The research directors are themselves former major contributors to science and are very liberal in approving projects. The screens they place over projects are primarily their applicability to company goals. The committees are all research committees. In this screening process (until budget reviews) they do not bring in outside operating people, although in something like 80% of their operating units the manager is a former research man.

Q. I think a research man has to be given a little freedom. Keep the committee out of it until the man has time to do things for himself.

A. I agree. The great problem is where to begin screening for feasibility to make sure that the man is not just tearing off in a fruitless direction.

Q. Do you have any recommendations on how to organize to clarify business objectives? How do you get research objectives to be laid down by corporate management?

A. An elaborate procedure used by a large company is described in the paper. The essence of this problem comes down to two processes — either "enunciation" or "appeal." If the managements do not perceive the needs for objectives, the enunciation process is likely to be out of the question. Lower level managers can try to encourage their bosses to get together and come up with goals, but this probably isn't going to get too far unless the top men think in such terms themselves.

I know of one situation where the research operation was literally at loose ends and couldn't get a feeling of where it was supposed to go and what its purpose was. So this particular group undertook the appeal route on purpose. It just kept putting proposals up to management: "We'd like to do this and can't do that. Why not?" Over a period of time research developed for itself a pattern of objectives which all could understand. This is one way of solving your problem.

If you cannot convince the management that clear objectives are needed — if they have not already recognized this themselves — there are other ways of getting research goals. The usual way is to sit down in some rather quiet place (like Buck Hill Falls) and try to work out a consistent pattern of some sort. I can think of one company that has taken this particular approach. Its top managers spent a whole week in this manner, then came back and put the defined objectives aside for a period of a month. Then they went back and spent another week on it, and so forth. Finally they came up with a package they thought was pretty good. Then they did a most extraordinary thing. They took the package of over-all company objectives and split it like this: They kept the total objectives to themselves — top management — and only handed out pieces of the objectives to one person in the operating organization, one piece to another man, and so on. How they expected this to keep coordination I'll never know, but at least the formulation stage of the objectives was rather well done.

Q. Isn't there a danger that top management is eager to do a big "objective setting job" but doesn't know what its objectives should be; so they get pushed into it and may set the wrong objectives?

A. It can certainly happen. However, you can always change the objective once it comes into being. You can do this by probing, by means of the proposal (or appeal) route. Although over-all objectives must be fairly permanent, you can always review these objectives if the company genuinely needs to be headed in a new direction.

Q. You formerly stressed the importance of stable objectives.

A. Objectives have to be changed over a period of time, but the time span is a several-year time span, and not a short-term, one-year, six-month, or three-month time span which is too common.

Q. You've emphasized "top management" all the way through here. You said nothing about operating divisions, divisional managers, and their responsibility for long-range planning.

A. My paper was purposely cut off at the level right above operating divisions. It seems fairly clear to me that if planning is to be done in a realistic sense, there has to be interplay. One company illustrates how this can be done. Its management first comes up with a set of objectives at the corporate level. These objectives then become the beginning point for the long-range planning process down in the operating division. They go out to each operating division manager. The operating division managers then draw up long-term plans which will meet these goals. As they draw up their long-term plans, if for any reason they feel that the goal itself may not be appropriate, the managers have the right to appeal the goal. They have, in effect, a contact man on the corporate level with whom they work in this connection. Final goals are worked out early in the planning process. Then the individual plans to meet these goals are fed up from the operating groups to a long-range planning committee at the corporate level.

The long-range planning committee's function is to take the plans which have come up from the operating divisions, work these together, and make sure that they mesh over the long period. They then convert, by means of staff units reporting to them, these long-range plans into a long-term capital plan. This is eventually approved at corporate level. The company maintains a decentralized operation despite this by not allowing *operating* budgets to be involved. It only allows capital budgets to come through this process, and the operating budgets are handled in an entirely separate fashion. Again, this exceedingly complex thing comes down to communications: One individual with a group; a group with one individual. It is a constant interplay situation and very difficult to sort out in a solid sense. There are a variety of ways it can be done, and it depends on the individuals involved.

Q. You have a very fine structure to your paper, and I have no criticism, but it has appeared organized around the consumer nondurable industry.

A. Would you like to develop this a little bit further? I had not particularly intended that this be the case. The examples I have chosen, I must confess, for probing out customer desires and things of this sort were chosen because it is easier to find good solid examples in certain fields.

Q. You've covered those industries and firms serving the consumer rather than those having a tradition of doing the research and producing new products before the customer can tell or is aware of what he needs or wants. Many firms are working in larger and larger systems and in different patterns of research.

(Comment) What you're saying is, I think, something along these lines: That the consumer doesn't really know what he wants in a finite sense. Consequently the company has to propose to the consumer that they have a product he might like before the consumer is aware of his own innate desires.

A. But, again, I think you could identify the parameters that are present. The consumer has certain desires — for example, entertainment, and for certain types of entertainment. These basic parameters are present. Certainly there was disagreement on whether television would be a wonderful thing or not all the way through, but basically there was a feeling that the consumer would some day like home video entertainment. Isn't that right?

Seriously, I do think that you have to approach any field with basically the same viewpoint: try to identify needs, desires, or wants where you can and work back into the development and applied research process. Obviously you will come up with ideas occasionally that are unique. Then you have to screen these ideas at various stages as they move forward from research into the expensive stages of development, scale up, and market introduction.

Q. (Smith) In our industry we've had two examples involving new physical phenomena. Nobody knew what they were going to do with that. No market research would tell. If you started with

market research, you'd be excluded from the business of the relatively new tehcnical material from which you eventually develop
products.

A. No, I'm not excluding this by any means. I'm saying that there are
two routes by which technology comes to the market. One route
is to identify a technological desire, want, or need. This is step
one — trying to find out about as many such things as you can;
then trying to work programs to fit them. Clearly, an applied
research program or fundamental research program that's really
successful is going to come up with technologies that you cannot
plan in advance. This is where the "bottom-up" planning process
occurs, when you first plan to get the technology. Then, when
you get the technology, you begin to screen it for its commercial
implications. I hope that you would agree with me that you don't
move these items into costly development stages until you have
made some market assessment even though these may be very
crude at first.

Q. One of the most important considerations when you plan the
program is to first decide the actual amount of dollars that you
can afford to spend on it. What's the criterion or procedure to go
about arriving at this answer?

A. I wish that I had a handy-dandy, homecooked solution for you
here. I do not know of any way except to go through project by
project, proposal by proposal, and analyze each in light of its
potential contributions to company goals and strategies. As the
project progresses it must be assessed against a range of criteria
which vary from very intuitive criteria (in the early stages) to
relatively precise mathematical criteria as you get way out to the
end of the development spectrum. Assess each one of these
proposals. If the item looks as though it's going to be useful and
have a value sufficiently greater than the cost of attaining it —
in an intuitive sense or however you have to measure this — you
should try to support the project. Again you have to pass the
project through a set of screens established by company goals —
and the limits of the company's capacity. You obviously can't
support all interesting projects and be predominant in all fields.
You simply have to expose yourself to some risks and pass up some
opportunities.

Q. But, if you go through this synthesis and come out with a number,
then don't you have to compare it with, say, the company's capabilities for generating capital? . . . If you tried to apply such a
criterion, it might turn out to be a pitifully small number.

A. Yes, this is certainly true.

Q. You've got to have a feedback whereby, having synthesized total program cost, you compare it against a framework of limitations.

A. Certainly. There are a number of checks. Essentially the process is to come up with a program package and compare it with your capacity limits.

Q. From your experience, Professor Quinn, how often do research planners get together with corporate management officers in order to determine the capital requirements with respect to technological research and long-range planning?

A. It can be simply at the time the research budgets come up for review. The financial officer may be involved only at this stage. In some cases, an over-all commitment as to general funds level is established before the research planning process begins. Then the package of programs is built up, and compared against the general funds limitation. The funds limitation may be changed or the package of products may be modified at the end of this cycle. There are many ways of doing these things. Financial considerations must get involved in any company to have integrated planning.

EVALUATION OF APPLIED
RESEARCH IN A BUSINESS FIRM

H. I. ANSOFF

H. I. ANSOFF

Vice President and General Manager
Information Technology Division
Lockheed Electronics Company
Metuchen, New Jersey

Dr. Ansoff was born in Russia of American parents and was educated at Stevens Institute where he received his M.E. degree in General Engineering and an M.S. degree in Mathematics and Physics. At Brown University he received his Ph.D. degree in Applied Mathematics. His career began in the teaching of physics and applied mathematics, including research on neo-military projects, until he joined the RAND Corporation in 1948. From that time until 1956 Dr. Ansoff participated in, and later directed, a succession of projects of increasing scope relative to technical opportunities, vulnerability, and strategies in connection with Air Force operations. in 1956 he joined Lockheed Aircraft Corporation and was assigned to make a basic analysis of their diversification problems. He became director of the Diversification Task Force at Lockheed in 1957, Vice President of Plans and Programs, Lockheed Electronics Company, in 1960, and since 1961 has been in the general management work of this subsidiary. He is the author of many analytical papers dealing with engineering, physics, mechanics, and, since 1957, business planning.

Evaluation of Applied Research
in a Business Firm

Applied Research as a Phase of the Product
Development Cycle

This paper is concerned with a framework for evaluation of applied research inside a business firm. One aim of such a framework is to provide a planning tool — a means for selecting from a list of competing research proposals those which will contribute most to the firm's profitability.

A second aim is to provide a control tool — a means by which accomplishment of selected projects can be monitored and controlled during their execution. The initial promise of the project must be continually re-evaluated against research results and other pertinent information which may develop. The project is then accelerated, decelerated, changed in direction or emphasis, or canceled altogether depending on the outcome of the evaluation. Thus, the contribution to the eventual profitability is optimized during the applied research phase.

Our concern is with applied research in business in contrast to other social institutions such as government, university, or a non-profit foundation. It must, therefore, be viewed against the background of business objectives and strategy. Two basic business objectives are essential parts of this background. The first of these postulates that a business firm is a *perpetual enterprise;* its basic aim is to survive forever. The second states that the central objective is to *maximize profitability over the long run.*[1]

A firm's product-market strategy is implemented through a series of sequential activities, usually referred to as the Product Development Cycle. Applied research is only one phase of this series of activities. In order to assess its contribution, therefore, it is necessary first to define the role of AR in the development cycle and to relate it to the phases which precede and follow.

---

[1] Conceptually, the first postulate defines the "long run" as infinity. In all practical situations, the long run is foreseeable business horizon — the maximum time period for which forecasts can be made. This concept is discussed in detail in a paper on *Business Objectives* by the author.

With that accomplished, a framework for evaluation of AR will follow naturally.

Definitions

The phase which occurs earliest in the development cycle is pure or basic research. Its result is creation of new knowledge which, in the physical sciences, is concerned with structural and dynamic properties of matter. It is the process of creating mathematical equations and/or experimental procedures which explain observable (man-made or nature-made) phenomena.

Applied research, which follows, is application of knowledge to solution of previously unsolved (usually generic) problems. It can either be device-oriented, such as a breadboard which demonstrates that optical diffractive properties of matter (knowledge) can be used to compress electromagnetic pulses (problem), or it can be technique-oriented, such as a procedure for growing semiconductor crystals.

Applied research is sometimes defined as application of knowledge to "useful" purposes. Such definition begs the central question of this paper; i.e., how to distinguish between "usefull" and "useless" AR projects. As we shall see, the word useful would rob the definition of its generic character, since what is useful to a business firm is not necessarily useful to a university.

Relation of Applied Research to the Development Cycle

The key characteristic implied in our definitions of applied research is the uncertainty of the outcome of a proposed project. Since the problem has not been solved before, the main object is to demonstrate that existing knowledge can be used to produce a solution.

The fact that the *degree* of uncertainty can vary over a wide spectrum gives rise to a major difficulty in defining clear-cut separation between AR and activities which precede and follow it. At one extreme, it is not uncommon to find applied research proposals whose outcome is so uncertain as to require, in fact, creation of new knowledge and which should, therefore, be recognized as basic research. The problem is not simply one of proper classification. Rather, it is one of determining the proper approach and proper talents to be employed. Failure to recognize the principal bottlenecks may lead to wasteful effort by engineers and model makers where mathematicians and theoretical physicists are called for. It may also lead to grossly overrun projects and badly missed schedules.

Confusion as to the true nature of applied research occurs most frequently at the other end of the spectrum of uncertainty where it may be confused with a later stage in the product development cycle, which is called product development. Product development is application of a known problem solution to construction of a device or development of a procedure to specific performance characteristics. It is the process of reduction to practice of results of applied research.

It is not infrequent to find a product development project mistakenly classified as applied research. As in the previous case, such confusion can result in much misplaced effort and in even further reaching consequences. The major problem arises from the fact that although AR and PD activities are very similar (involving, usually, construction of a working device), their purposes are entirely different. The former is merely to show that a particular problem can be solved; the latter is to start a chain of steps which eventually lead to offering a product to potential customers. Whereas applied research may sometimes be justifiable if it merely holds a promise of a substantial improvement in the state-of-the-art, product development is *never* justifiable unless it holds promise of making a profit for the company. Unless, prior to undertaking product development, an effort is made to determine the potential profitability, the result will be very high product mortality and hence a waste of research and development funds.

When an applied research project is successfully completed, it yields only one essential part of the information required for determining potential profitability. AR merely tells us that a particular *type* of device can be built or a fabrication technique used to produce a particular type of product. Missing at this point are the following essential pieces of information: does a demand exist for this type of device (or product); what *specific* performance characteristics are desired; how does performance relate to the price the customers are willing to pay; how is performance related to our costs to make the device; what competing devices are already available; how does our device compare with them; what will it cost us to put the product on the market.

If these additional questions can be answered satisfactorily, the results must be integrated into an over-all estimate of two central factors in product development decisions — the *potential return on investment* and the *associated risks* which will be incurred on the way to product commercialization.

Although central, ROI and risk estimates are not sufficient for they measure the proposed product taken *by itself* apart from the company's other products and markets. Further questions must be examined in order to determine the *strategic fit* of the proposed product: does it fit the company's over-all product-market strategy, or will it necessitate a change in strategy; how does it relate to the present product-market position; what joint economies and diseconomies will result; how does the timing of its introduction fit in with introduction to or withdrawal from the market of the company's other products.

Thus, in addition to success in applied research, a host of other requirements, fully as important to future success, must be met before a product development effort is justified. It becomes apparent that applied research is only a part of a phase in the product development cycle which represents transition from basic research to product development. Other parts of the phase are:

1. *Applications Analysis* (sometimes called systems analysis) which is concerned with the translation of customer needs into product performance specifications, as well as with studies of economic justification of the product from the point of view of the customer.

2. *Market Research*, which analyzes the demand, the competitive factors, and the pricing structure as well as the marketing costs.

3. *Applications Research* (sometimes called preliminary design) which translates the performance specification into a specific technical design and an estimate of the development and manufacturing costs.

4. *Business Analysis*, which consolidates all the preceding factors into an analysis of profit potential, risks, and the strategic fit.

In a given project, any one of these factors may be equally as or even more important than applied research. The rate of mortality of development projects is directly related to the ability of the planning organization to isolate ingredients of the product research phase which are critical to success. For example, if the probability of success of applied research looms high, but it is not clear that there is an existing demand for the potential results, market research may be indicated as the primary activity.

The related activities described above are directed toward answering a central question, which is: should the firm undertake development of a suggested product? Applied research is one of these aspects, dealing, as it does, with a question of whether existing knowledge can be used to produce the type of performance desired of the product. Other aspects inquire into economic and business factors involved. The entire complex of activities is then appropriately named *product research.*

The question of whether applied research should precede, follow, or be performed concurrently with other parts of the product research phase depends on the particular situation. In firms which have a long history of participation in a particular market, whose product technology is relatively stable, and whose growth is primarily through development of new products to supersede earlier models, applied research would normally come first. Pursuit of other parts may not be essential to success because, through long-time familiarity with its products and markets, the firm has built up a large fund of product research information.

On the other hand, firms which are relatively new to their markets, which are participating in a dynamic technology, and which grow largely through product diversification, need to give priority to other parts of product research. In such cases, successful applied research alone will not be sufficient to give indications of the profitability and strategic value of the proposed project.

Evaluation of Profitability

Since applied research is an integral part of product research, evaluation of proposed AR projects should be subject to the same basic criteria which apply to the over-all phase. At the same time, the information usually available at the inception of an applied research project is sparse and uncertain and not adequate for a definitive evaluation of potential profitability. For this reason, our approach to evaluation of applied research will be first to construct an over-all framework for evaluation of

profitably and then to modify it to take account of the uncertainties in the information.

Figure 1-A represents a typical history of required investment
in the course of a product development cycle for a specific
product. The earliest phase is product research. It may or may
not involve applied research activity. At the termination of this
phase, desirability of further development is evaluated, and the
product development phase is initiated which terminated with
successful construction of an engineering prototype. Following
this, product engineering takes over. A production prototype is
built, production drawings are prepared and proofed, manufacturing facilities are planned and installed, build-up of inventories
begins, and a marketing plan is prepared and put into action.

As the curve suggests, the rate of investment into the new
product progressively accelerates toward the end of product
engineering phase and then levels off as the product begins to
show profit.

From that point on, investment recovery takes place in accordance with an amortization schedule which is usually based
on a conservative estimate of the useful life of the product. If
it does turn out to be conservative, then, for a period, investment
will level off at the value of the working capital and unamortized
fixed assets which are required to support the product. Toward
the end of the product's life, further investment recovery takes
place through liquidation of inventories.

Figure 1-B shows the corresponding history of the return on
investment. This remains at zero through the product engineering cycle and then usually turns negative for a time while the
learning costs are absorbed. Following, the return on investment
builds up rapidly to a more or less steady state level and declines
to zero toward the end of the useful life of the product.

Figures 1-A and 1-B suggest that the following basic variables
describe the value of the product to the sponsoring firm:

1. The average return on investment over the product lifetime. This is the basic measure of desirability.
2. The maximum investment that will have to be incurred,
   since this determines the drain on the company's resources.
3. The payout period, which is the time to full recovery of
   investment, on the assumption that all the product's earnings

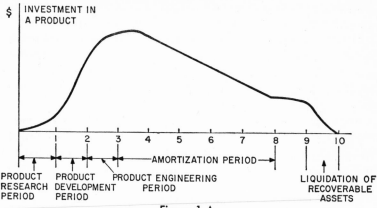

Figure 1-A

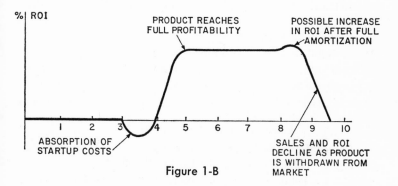

Figure 1-B

are used for this purpose, since this is an indication of how long the investment will be tied up.

4. The time to reach the maximum return on investment, since this indicates the product enters its earning period.
5. The life span, since it indicates duration of this period.
6. Last, but first in importance, the risks that will be incurred on the way to investment recovery.

A Framework for Evaluation of Applied Research

As mentioned earlier, the difficulty in evaluating profitability of applied research stems from the fact that the decision has to be made very near the beginning of the cycle, when the information available is at its worst. In a majority of cases, the data are insufficient to attempt even an approximate computation of the return on investment. One way to get around this difficulty is to set up a number of individual criteria which are related to the basic elements of profitability, to evaluate the proposed applied research project in the light of each one of these, and then to combine the results into an over-all figure of merit which is generally proportional to the return on investment. A similar figure of merit is established for a measure of the risk.

The criteria shown below are broken down into two classes. The first is related to the numerator of the return on investment fraction, and hence to potential profit. The second is related to the denominator, and hence to the required investment.

Criteria Related to Potential Earnings

I Profit Potential
   — Estimate of total sales (earnings) over lifetime (E)
   — Technological Merit (M_t)
   — Business Merit (M_b)
II Probability of success of project (P_s)
III Probability of successful market penetration (P_p)
IV Strategic fit of proposed project with other projects, products, and markets of the company (S)

Criteria Related to Investment

I Direct Investment ($C_{ar} + C_{pr} + C_{pd} + C_{pe} + WC + F = C_d$)
   C_{ar} = Total cost of applied research effort
   C_{pr} = Total cost of product research effort (exclusive of applied research)
   C_{pd} = Total cost of product development effort
   C_{pe} = Total cost of product engineering effort
   WC = Working capital required
   F = Total cost of extra facilities required such as staff, buildings, etc.
II Joint Cost Effect (J)
   J = Savings factor in direct investment resulting from use or sharing of existing facilities and capabilities

Within the first class, the first criterion is profit potential. The ideal measurement would be to estimate the earnings potential which will result from the proposed research. Since this may not be possible, the rating on this criterion is obtained from three estimates:

a. An approximate estimate of total sales (or earnings), which can be seen as the direct foreseeable result of the proposed research venture.

b. Technological merit, which ranks the project in terms of the contribution it can make to the state-of-the art.

c. Business merit, which estimates the breadth of business opportunity which will be opened up as a result of successful research.

All three of these factors are based on an estimate of the intrinsic merit of the proposed project, without reference to the performing organization and under the assumptions that the project will be successful and that a successful market penetration can be made.

The second major factor is to estimate the probability of success of the proposed applied research project. This is based on recognition of bottleneck technical problems which need to be overcome by research, on the clarity of the proposed approach to the solution, on past experience in similar types of research, and on availability and quality of technical skills available for the project.

The third major factor is another conditional probability. It is the probability that, if the project is technically successful, a successful market penetration can be made. The estimate here is based on two major considerations. The first is the nature of the competitive environment: similar research efforts being performed elsewhere, their quality, and the strength of the companies behind them. Second is an estimate of the competitive capabilities of the sponsoring company. This includes existence of the required type of manufacturing, development, and sales competence.

The fourth factor which affects the estimated potential earnings is what we have previously referred to as strategic fit. It measures the contribution of the proposed project to the desired strategic direction of the company. It measures the joint economies and diseconomies which may result in conjunction with development of other products and performance of other research within the company. Finally, it determines the desirability of the timing of the product introduction with respect to the other products of the company.

The second class of criteria is related to the investment that will be incurred in the course of the complete life cycle. First is the investment required for the proposed applied research project. In addition, it is necessary to estimate the costs of the remainder of the product research cycle: product development, product engineering, capital investment, and working capital which will be required to sustain the product. In the early stages of the product development cycle, it may be extremely difficult to estimate most of these costs with any degree of precision. However, order of magnitude estimates can have a very significant influence on the decision to proceed with an applied research project.

For example, a firm which is contemplating research in the field of digital computer techniques must give serious consideration to logical consequence of such work. Research on techniques will lead to development of computers. Successful entry into the computer field has traditionally required a multimillion dollar investment. If the company does not have sufficient resources to provide for such expense, it may well choose to forego research in this direction.

The second element of investment is a measure of the joint economies and diseconomies which may follow introduction of the product. This involves possible joint use of existing facilities, machinery, distribution channels, et cetera. On the negative side, the proposed project may call for the use of critical research skills which are in demand on other products.

The evaluation of the individual criteria can be performed by assigning an arbitrary scale to each and ranking competing projects on that scale. Following this, they are combined in an overall figure of merit:

$$\text{Figure of Merit (profit)} = \text{FM}_p = \frac{(M_t + M_b) \times E \times P_s \times P_p}{C_d \times J} \times S$$

This adds the rankings of the technical and business merits and applies them as an adjustment to the estimate of the sales potential. These are then multiplied by the respective measures of probabilities of success of the project and probability of market penetration. The product is divided by the estimate of the investment which is adjusted by a factor estimating joint economies and diseconomies. This gives a figure of merit which approximates profitability of the proposed project taken by itself. To obtain the impact on other products and markets of the company, this fraction is multiplied by the strategic fit rating.

In addition to the figure of merit which is related to profitability, a comparably important yardstick is a measure of risk involved in undertaking the proposed research:

$$\text{Figure of Merit (risk)} = FM_r = \frac{C_{ar}}{FM_p}$$

This is approximated by the ratio of the cost of the proposed research to the over-all figure of merit. Very roughly speaking, this is the dollar cost at risk in applied research per percent of eventual return on investment.

The framework for evaluation of applied research described above has the obvious disadvantages of lack of precision and the dangers which stem from ordinal rankings. Furthermore, it is well known that use of fractions as a figure of merit without particular attention being paid to the behavior of the numerator and denominator can lead to erroneous conclusions.

Nevertheless, in view of the usual limitations on information available at the initiation of applied research, the proposed method has the following merits:

1. It provides a mechanism for anticipating costs and problems which can arise subsequent to research.
2. It permits a relative ranking of competing applied research projects.
3. It makes possible a comparison of applied research to other phases of product research.
4. It places applied research within the over-all business perspective of the firm.

Summary

The purpose of this paper has been to discuss the role of applied research within a business firm and to place it in the context of the over-all product development cycle. Applied research was compared to basic research, on the one hand, and to product development, on the other. It was pointed out that applied research is only a part of a phase which is intermediate between basic research and product development. This product research phase was shown to consist of the following basic ingredients: applied research, applications analysis, market research, preliminary design, and business analysis. It was pointed out that the decision of whether applied research must precede or accompany

other phases of product research should be made in the light of
the particular product-market position of the firm.

It was pointed out that an early identification of those ingredients of product research which critically affect profitability
is one of the most important tools in product planning.

An over-all framework for evaluation of profitability of a new
product throughout its life cycle was presented. With this as
background, an approximate method for evaluation of applied research projects was presented which is designed to allow for the
uncertainties and lack of knowledge usually present at the inception of applied research projects.

Q. I want to know why you put S in that equation. After all, why do
you care about the strategic fit? Isn't it true that you care because
poor fit will force you into new areas of costs? Those are already
reflected in C and D and perhaps in J. So, if you diagnose those
right, where's the significance of strategic fit?

A. "Fit" is a central notion. I noticed that Mr. Smith talked about
it . . . and so did Dr. Herwald. If, whenever a new business opportunity comes along, we were smart enough to investigate its
complete ramifications, going back into the past and into the
future of the company, there would be no need for strategy. All
I'd need to do is have my profitability objective. The proposal
that rings the bell highest in the scale would be the thing that
I'd pick. The reason we are forced into strategy is essentially the
uncertainty in whatever evaluations we make. Therefore, when
I go through the exercise of strategic fit, in effect, I kind of make
a lame duck allowance. It implicitly implies aspects of the Js,
the Cs, of D's that I may not be explicitly able to take care of in
the equation. Another way of putting it, when we evaluate the
rest of this formula, we are primarily concerned with the consequences of the product in question being taken by itself, as if the
company had no other products on the market. The upward or
downward adjustment in the return provided by S places this
product into the overall perspective of the product line.

Q. It's a reflection of your uncertainty relative to the proposal because
the project is not a part of your traditional operating area.

A. I think not. I think it's a reflection of uncertainty relative to the
fact that none of us know a hell of a lot about our businesses. We
don't have a way of explaining business to ourselves. We don't
have a way of computing consequences of our actions.

Q. Could we name again the things you've considered under strategic fit?

A. Let me see what I have in the text and that will keep me from making a long-winded answer. No, I took care of it very nicely. I said that "to obtain the impact of other products and markets of the company, this fraction is multiplied by the strategic fit rate!" Seriously speaking, it has to stem, as Professor Quinn pointed out, from the definition of what a strategy is. To me a strategy is a very simple notion — it's a set of rules for selecting among investment opportunities that present themselves to you. It's the kind of rules that are going to optimize your company's objectives. Any of the definitions of Professor Quinn's strategy would fit, for example. If my company has made a success, strategically speaking, by being indispensable to the customer, then my measurement of whether this further contributes to my indispensability to the customer would give me an additional measure of confidence or lack thereof in the estimate of the various other factors in the formula, resulting in an upward or downward adjustment of the figure of merit. I'm sorry this reply is so long-winded, but it's because I don't understand it too well!

Q. We've been working in this field, too, and we've come up with equally vague mathematical expressions, containing equally vague parameters. Yours is about the same chart, so far as I can see.

A. You use them? Do you believe them?

Q. Yes. (Sotto voce)

Q. What's the advantage of putting all these things into a complex formula when you have the problem of the *J* factor going to zero or something like that? Where your controls go out the window? Why not take into account these factors by listing them and thinking about them rigorously. Then coming up with what amounts to a present value analysis of the particular project.

A. This *is* a present value analysis.

Q. I just wondered why go into the final formlua? Why not simply rank proposals by the present value or rank by the return on present value?

A. This is a very relevant question. I think this is the kind of thing that makes some of us feel that we must strive toward a theory and some of us feel that we must go through business life by the case method. I'm not confusing you with a case method advocate entirely, but there are some of them in the vicinity.

One of the smartest mathematicians I know (I think he is a Harvard man) says that God has created all relations in only two shapes — they're either constants or they are linear. He's obviously fibbing, but I think that the point he's making is that the human mind is very improperly constituted because it can't think of more than three things at any given time. Therefore, if you want to find any correlation between two human minds, it is important to reduce the thing that you are considering to some common understandable framework about which you can both argue and disagree. Essentially this is why you attempt to reduce the expression to the over-all profitability figures. I don't know what you mean by present value analysis. . . . This *is* an attempt at present value analysis. This is also an attempt to combine factors into a kind of over-all judgment factor which goes up, in general, when profitability goes up; which goes down, in general, when profitability goes down. You get this kind of correlation. I think it's a matter of individual preference as to which way one likes to look at the universe.

Q. We're not really talking about the same thing. . . . I think present value adds a refinement on this general approach.

A. I think we'd better attempt to define precisely what we're talking about.

Q. You can do this by discounting the cash flows and profitability.

A. All you are doing is to apply some more correction factors to this analysis because what you discount is this equation.

Q. Isn't an element of judgment working all through here? The element of judgment is associated with each one of those subjects.

A. Oh, unquestionably. If I would call this science, my alma mater — Brown — would hear about it and they'd take my sheepskin away. No, this is an attempt to set up some common grounds within which people can make judgments. You don't go out and hire a brand new kid that's never been in a sales department or has never done research and say, "All right, kiddo, here's the formula and here's a bunch of research projects — now what are they worth? . . . This is for people of maturity and judgment. The only implied issue that we are raising here is whether you want to organize your universe in this manner so that, for a change, it would be almost comprehensible.

Q. Wouldn't your item, the estimate of total sales, be affected by what's in the back of your mind and all other factors in the numerator?

A. Don't you think this equation is terribly nonlinear?

Q. Yes, if you want to put it that way.

A. I don't want to put it that way. I just thought maybe we could communicate in the "right way." One tries to estimate the total demand situation independently of his participation in it. As the second step one tries to deal with the probability of market penetration.

Q. Dr. Ansoff, you have the same thing written down, in a sense. How can you estimate the total sales figures unless you have something in the back of your mind as to its technological merit figure? So, what I'm trying to say is that: When you break this down, you can't help being influenced by both of these factors unless you combine them explicitly. So you may want to put the equation in a simpler fashion.

A. Yes, I'll put it in a simpler fashion: This is a well-known peril and we're all subject to it. There are two issues here, I think. One is the awkward way in which I answered the earlier question. The answer to that is "yes" or "no," depending on what you define by these various terms. The other is the issue of practical application of this equation, and of getting yourself into the frame of mind so that when you're working on E, you're not worrying about P_f. My personal experience in this kind of thing has been that this is a difficult problem. As a result, what you find yourself doing is going through each item three or four times over because you catch yourself allowing judgment that you've already exercised to influence the judgment on another factor. There's no question about this. One of the things one tries to do when a group operates trying to solve a problem like this is to define as explicitly as one can, on a piece of paper, as to what we shall mean by E, and what we shall mean by P_s. That helps some, I think, but you're absolutely right about the interacting effect of judgments.

Q. What about the relative weighting of these different factors? It seems to me that it may be impossible to do anything with this or that factor. One has to know whether M_t is more important than P_s or vice versa. This is the essence of business judgment.

A. I'm not sure I understand the question.

Q. Of these different factors that are listed, what weights does the user give to these different factors? Which ones are relatively more important and which ones less? This would seem of great importance.

A. Yes, indeed. Whenever you try to do this analysis it comes up almost automatically. It has come up in some of the exercises we've gone through here. I think it's perfectly obvious that when you set up the ordinal scales, you may assign ranges from 1 to 10 to this number and from 1 to 100 in that number. The manner in which you assign them is going to lean very heavily upon where you happen to find yourself in the business situation. I agree with you there. A great many more things could be done in ranking.

Q. Have you checked this retroactively in a couple of successful ventures?

A. I can claim one.

Q. How did it come out?

A. Very good. I must confess also that it was a real honey and even if it didn't apply any R & M formulas to it, we probably never will be sorry.

Q. We've mentioned a figure of merit on this program. How do you use it? . . . There are many people who immediately assign fact to a number . . .

A. I think that it's further-reaching than this. I think there's a tendency to be fascinated with the sound of your own ratings.

Q. Do you have a time factor specified in your equation?

A. It's implied by an attempt to estimate the total return over the life cycle of the product. This can be written in three or four different ways depending on how crude or how fancy you want to get. You can compress this expression, you can expand that expression, having essentially the same form. You can for example, go for simple exercises in the use of this equation by studying a relationship as a function of the position in the life cycle of the product. So our figure of merit becomes a variable. You can actually plot some graphs and see when this or that factor is going to do something for you and when it is going to hurt you. This will determine the capital requirement planning.

Q. This is an approach which, under certain circumstances, is very appealing to me. I've developed such an equation, but there are some limitations to it that I think you haven't used. In trying to evaluate the relative merits of roughly twenty different projects we set up a limited *ad hoc* group. The results then were *ad hoc* results, and were only relatively true at that period of time for that particular project. A few years later a different group runs the same exercise with the same definition of the variability and the quantitative development of each factor before the rating takes place. They then review these twenty projects. The value judgments they set up on the order of magnitude between one project and the next were consistent with the original effort. As far as we know we missed only one. For relative rating of these projects, I thought this was excellent.

A. We're doing a thing like this in one of our units and presenting it to intermediate management. This was when I was in the fortunate business of being in staff and looking up. Another way of putting it is that an approach like this has to be interpreted and a judgment framework established before it's brought up for decision.

EVALUATING THE RESULTS
OF RESEARCH

JAMES W. HACKETT

HARRY H. HOLSCHER

JAMES W. HACKETT

Vice President Administrative-Research and Engineering
Owens-Illinois Glass Company
Toledo, Ohio

Mr. Hackett holds a B.S. in Engineering and Physics from Ohio State University. After work in the Research Laboratories of General Motors Corporation as a physical metallurgist, he joined Owens-Corning Fiberglas, and served briefly with the Victor Adding Machine Company as Assistant Director of Research. Since 1947, he has progressed through process development, general research, and new product development departments of Owens-Illinois Glass Company. He became Director of Research in 1953 and was recently promoted to his present position. As the head of a special committee for the Industrial Research Institute, he conducted a detailed study of methods of evaluating research proposals and results for the member firms of that organization.

Mr. Hackett listed Dr. Harry H. Holscher, Staff Scientist-Research and Engineering, as his co-author.

Evaluating the Results of Research

Last winter, three two-day study conferences upon methods and procedures for the evaluation of research were conducted by the Industrial Research Institute. One of the purposes of the Industrial Research Institute is to promote, through the cooperative efforts of its members, improved, economical, and effective techniques of the organization, of the administration, and the operation of industrial research. Fifty-seven persons, representing nearly that many companies, participated in these conferences. As co-chairman of these conferences, the senior author was invited to discuss this subject. Some of the results of these conferences will be presented, but, furthermore, our own views will supplement this discussion. This paper, therefore, does not represent an official report of the proceedings of the IRI conferences. It departs somewhat from the limitations of the conference in presenting our own views of the subject The official report of last winter's conferences will appear in *Research Management,* published by the Industrial Research Institute.

There is an extremely widespread interest in techniques used for the evaluation of the research operation. Both top management and research management have been concerned with the problem for some time. Even though formal techniques may be a recent trend, there has always been some effort made to determine the effectiveness of the research and development operation.

The interest of top management has recently intensified. According to the National Science Foundation data,[1] research and development expenditures in the United States rose from $5.15 billion in 1953 to $12.43 billion in 1959. Various estimates place the expected expenditures in 1970 between $20 and $25 billion. This rapidly increasing outlay of money has been brought into even sharper focus by the recent intensification of the profit squeeze. Top management is asking: (1) whether research investments are worthwhile at all, (2) how research returns compare with those of alternate investment opportunities, and (3) whether

[1] *Reviews of Data on Research & Development,* No. 26, February 1961.

227

the scientific effort is proceeding with maximum effectiveness. While the research director has a vital interest in the first two questions, he is continuously concerned with the third question.

We will initiate our study by describing the why, when, and where of the problem, proceeding on to methods of approach in the IRI studies, and then attempt to list many of the contributions of research to an organization. These contributions will be broken down by those which can be evaluated in dollars and thence to those which show a definite contribution not readily evaluated in dollars. The effects of the research and development department upon the viewpoints of the company from the standpoint of the scientist, the general public, and the internal company organization are to be presented.

Some propositions concerning the evaluation of research which can be of great aid to anyone considering the development of a formal evaluation system will be considered.

A typical evaluation system which, with minor variations, is now used in a fair number of companies, will be discussed. The cash flow profile chart offers a method of evaluating projects before they are initiated, during their prosecution, and after they have been completed by the research department. Such charts can be carried through the phases of engineering and into production. Finally, the possibilities and value of research evaluation in relation to over-all company planning and objectives will be discussed.

*   *   *   *   *

The problem of evaluation must be faced quite early. Research is a part of business and must be evaluated as a part of business and for its own survival.

It is wise, where possible, to attempt to evaluate the research problem before the program is set. At this stage, the projection of a cash flow profile chart (which we will discuss later) should be attempted. The outlining of the specific objectives and the mode of approach to the problem are quite important. An applied research program which has been developed in order to satisfy certain company objectives is most helpful.

As the research proceeds, views on success or failure of accomplishment gradually become clearer. A continuous evaluation concerning such expectations will allow one to determine whether the rate of activity and accomplishments are compatible. One may then decide to step up the rate of activity, or to decrease the rate of activity, or perhaps even stop the project. Such decisions are most difficult in research and development, and are often made strictly on the facts available at a given time without regard to the relationship of those facts to the original objective, or the rate of approach to that objective. Two questions should be asked regarding any project before the project is initiated: (1) if the problem is satisfactorily solved, do the benefits warrant the projected effort in time and money, and (2) from a technical point of view, does the expected solution look reasonably feasible? During the course of the project, whenever the rate of effort is being considered, the following questions should be asked: (3) in the light of our present knowledge, what are the answers to questions 1 and 2 above, and (4) if both answers are yes, is the rate of progress toward the goal satisfactory?

A continued study of economic aspects, market, consumer, cost, and selling price is necessary. Research emphasis may change due to a change in company policy, or to any number of other factors. After the project has been completed, the effort is made to put dollars and cents on the benefits to be obtained. One then also arrives at a concept of the efficiency of the research operation itself.

In the IRI conferences, the chairmen felt that the study groups could best approach the problem through the following steps:

(1) Generation of a list of all contributions of research and development to a business enterprise with some classification as to their amenability to quantitative or qualitative evaluation.

(2) A discussion of some of the methods used for quantitative or qualitative evaluation by companies represented.

(3) Drawing generalized propositions concerning the evaluation of research and development.

The contributions of research and development which are felt to be more directly evaluable in dollars are products, processes, raw materials, costs, and competition. Old products can be analyzed from the standpoint of the maintenance of the present product line or the broadening of the line. Process improvement and the development of new processes for old products can be given dollars and cents evaluation.

New products may require new processes. Old products can receive dollar evaluation when processes are altered or replaced. Any specific company is acquainted with the characteristics of the raw materials which they use. The usage of alternate materials can generally receive direct dollar evaluation. The usage of a higher grade material may improve the process or the product.

The development of new products may produce a market and thence profits where none existed. The two mainstays in relation to profit improvement are quality and cost. Process changes must result in improved quality and/or decreased costs. Once again, money is not spent on new processes unless there is an expectation of profits.

One cannot separate cost and competition from the product, process, and raw material aspects. The concept of lower costs or improved quality implies many other direct relationships within the company organization. If a new product uses the present manufacturing facilities or the present distribution system, it can become profitable much more quickly. We are thus making better use of extensive previously acquired know-how of the organization and the people.

From a competitive standpoint, research can often contribute by the development of patentable features which may be easily evaluated in dollars and cents. Perhaps even direct dollars through sales of patent rights is possible. In addition, a position of competitive trading may be attainable.

The ideas related to products, processes, raw materials, cost factors, and competition are to a large degree evaluable directly in dollars. This is not only a job for management, but contributions from research and development personnel on the impact of competitive technologies are important. The technical person may have useful views on the future competitive situation.

Many factors of a technical nature have influence throughout the company. Some of these factors are concerned more with the technical profile of the company; some are concerned with the over-all general company profile; and some are internal aspects within the company organization.

Consider, first, the technical profile as described by the following list:

The Technical Profile

Basic Technology	Product Promotion
Technical Intelligence	Diversification
Contract Research	Flexibility
Customer Usage	Government Regulation
Competition Comparisons	Technical Recruiting

Technical Publications

For instance, a fundamental research group will develop basic technology and technical intelligence which is conducive to ideas. Contract research also creates such technical aspects. Even though it may be entered into as a direct specific profit deal, it has an influence on the over-all technical intelligence of the company. While contract research for profit is a business itself, it does often create ideas of use within the company.

Other aspects of direct value to the company are the competitive and the customers' views of that company. Customers definitely prefer to deal with companies which are known for their advancing technology and research and development. They feel that they get something either directly or indirectly from a supplier's research and development activities. Competition is easy if one is the leader both in the product and the process and in the research. Product promotion is often associated with technology aspects.

The diversification of a company because of the presence of an idea-producing department can become important. More flexibility is obtained from the use of two or three associated ideas rather than one well-spent and outmoded concept.

Technical recruiting for research personnel is made easier by the presence of a research group with known reputation and with a tangible list of technical publications. The attraction to the scientist, who hopes to continue publication, is an intangible asset.

We therefore take the view that a company, just like a human being, must be complete in all its aspects for survival in the competitive world. In 10 or 20 years, the view may be obvious that perhaps three-quarters of the sales value is in ideas not existing today.

A broadminded and complete company contributes to the public welfare, to an increased standard of living, and at the same time has a proper attitude toward the customer, the employee, and the investor. Research and development contribute to these aspects of public interest, and every improvement in quality or decrease in cost results in an improved standard of living. Automation has almost always resulted in extensive volume improvement and quite often attainment of certain markets which can be reached in no other fashion. While the American standard of living is high, everybody still has a large "want" list. We can consume much more than we now do.

Some contributions which result from the technical effort are not normally considered a function of the research and development departments. Contributions are made to the morale and prestige of a company, to its public relations, to its recruiting and training for nontechnical departments, and toward assistance in purchasing activities, legal activities, safety, etc. Improved creativity comes from the company personnel as a whole. Such contributions cannot easily be assessed as to value: they are a by-product of the main effort. Let us list them as "associated R & D contributions."

Associated R &D Contributions to the Company Organization

Morale and Prestige	Legal and Patent
Public Relations	Miscellaneous Services
Recruiting and Training	Safety
Purchasing	Technical Intelligence

Inspires Creativity

We have discussed some of the tangible and intangible benefits of research; we shall now proceed to a discussion of the evaluation process.

It seems quite obvious that evaluation is important but perhaps we need to review some aspects of this phase:

(a) It is now recognized that research is an integral partner in the existence and growth of a company. Under today's highly competitive conditions, the management of research, as well as associated company management, is looking for more sophisticated tools for the evaluation of research.

(b) Research and development has an important effect upon the cash flow of a company. The development of a cash flow profile chart (as shown later) brings into focus the heavy expenditures of a major development, and their association to future production which uses the development, into an ultimate profit situation.

(c) Evaluation of past results, particularly when compared with past pre-evaluation, is beneficial in sharpening pre-evaluation methods; it gives the research director a measurement of the efficiency of the research and development operation, and gives the research and development personnel a measure of their effectiveness and contribution.

(d) There are very definite and tangible benefits from attempts to evaluate research and development broadly. Those who are using evaluation techniques are convinced that they are benefiting in the research process itself, *as well as in other areas of the business.* Generally the methods used are based on the project approach.

(e) Better records and better feedback of costs and profits or losses in most cases are necessary for improved evaluation. Additional administrative effort and expense are generally involved in proper evaluation.

(f) Evaluation focuses attention on new product output and assists in making management aware of pitfalls and care necessary to bring new products to profitable marketing. Not all research is successful; neither can the cost be pre-evaluated to a high degree of accuracy. The inherent time lag in research and development must be taken into consideration. The time value of money must be considered in judging the value of the proposed investment.

Concerning the techniques of evaluation, we must recognize several aspects given below:

(a) No accurate and universally applicable evaluation techniques are available nor do they appear on the horizon; however, all research can be evaluated in an abstract or subjective sense by comparing the list of possible contributions and accomplishments with a pre-established set of objectives and criteria for success. Certain aspects of research are measurable in dollars to a usable degree of accuracy.

(b) Evaluation can be carried out only if criteria for success can be established. This should be in dollars wherever practical. In any event, a clear statement of research targets or objectives should be set forth. Even though a dollar evaluation seems successful, a crosscheck evaluation system involving nonprofit dollar objectives, criteria for success, and methods of functioning should also be used. This is because the final dollar profits do not depend upon the research and development effort alone. It is possible to have a highly competent and successful research and development effort in a company showing poor profit performance because of the inadequacy of other departments. On the other hand, a very poor research and development department might not adversely affect the profits of a company with a good present technical position and outstanding departments such as sales, manufacturing, etc.

(c) In all methods, judgment is a dominant factor in establishing the research and development contributions.

(d) Methods of evaluation should be in terms clear to top management since they are giving it more attention.

(e) The absolute direct dollar results of research, except in some very limited cases, cannot be completely isolated from the efforts of other members of the business team such as the general management, sales, product, marketing, planning, legal, finance, and personnel departments.

(f) Evaluation should be on a long-term basis. Short-term evaluation should be viewed with caution.

(g) Relatively little work has been done on the evaluation of defensive research in maintaining a competitive position, yet this is highly important.

We shall now proceed to outline the different phases of a typical evaluation procedure. In instituting an evaluation technique, one progresses from the fundamental phase or basic research phase to an idea which must be evaluated. One feels that the idea can be made to work with further applied research and development. The feasibility study of the idea therefore occurs quite early in the time schedule. At this point, or perhaps a little later, contacts are made with the operating division who would pick up the development, taking it to a product stage. These contacts involve an appraisal of the feasibility of the idea, how the idea fits the company profile, and a multitude of other aspects before further development money is spent. We then proceed to the stage of applied research and development which is probably the most expensive stage of the technical phases. If this research is successful, the project is engineered and transferred to an operating division. Feasibility studies have been continuous since the early statement of the idea.

The idea, which has now become a definite project of the operating division, must be transferred from the research group. Top management, the operating division management, and research must all agree on certain aspects for evaluation. This stage starts as early as the idea is expressed. The degree of responsibility for the transfer to the operating division (from research, engineering, and production) must be definitely stated. At this time a credit to research, based on percentage of the returns, must also be thrashed out. The time limit on this credit will then determine what proportion of the return can be allocated for evaluation purposes for a technical credit, thus writing off the research and development cost. The efficiency of the research operation and the benefits of the research operation become evident.

The third phase of evaluation involves the commercial operation for a number of periods — say years — together with a split of the profits which are divided into credits for the operation and credits for the technical phase. Over a period of some time (as previously agreed to) these profits are calculated and the credits made.

This system will probably require modification of accounting procedures to isolate the essential data. The system demands administrative efforts on a continuing and dynamic basis. The scientists see the effects of their work and build a stature from it. The biggest question here is the split of the credits toward operation and technical ends. This is a delicate question but it can be handled through mutual respect and goodwill. It demands subjective judgment.

The above illustrations of a typical evaluation give an idea of the problems involved. When the system is carried to the most desirable conclusion, there evolves what might be considered the most universal chart which we call a cash flow profile chart (Figure 1). Here, the numbers on the chart indicate various steps of the effort as follows.

A UNIVERSAL SYSTEM ?
CASH FLOW

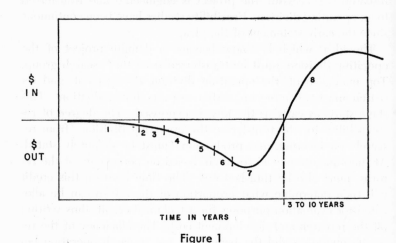

TIME IN YEARS

Figure 1

1. Research
2. Commercial invention
3. Feasibility proof
4. Development

5. Engineering
6. Capital investment
7. Production
8. Payoff

Note that the rate of expenditure of dollars is increasing steadily through each of the first six phases. Also note that it is the general consensus that from three to ten years may be required before the returns offset the cash outflow. After the payoff, the curve is shown descending in profit, based on the probability of another major development displacing what has at that time become the standard business.

One of the most informative and helpful systems for evaluating research is through the projection and refinement of a cash flow profile. At some stage in research a commercial invention is generated. Once that specific application of information is envisioned, one can start projecting the total cost of its development and commercialization in the market place. The curve in Figure 1 shows that through (1) research, (2) commercial invention, (3) feasibility proof, (4) development, (5) engineering, and (6) capital investment for production, there is an ever-increasing flow of cash out of the company's liquid assets. When production (7) gets underway and becomes profitable, one gets a return of this invested cash. At some time, as indicated in the chart, all of the cash will be returned and thereafter profits will be generated (8), developing liquid assets which are the payoff for the previous work and investment in the project.

It can be seen that if one could accurately forecast these profiles for a given project, it would be very easy to sort out among a group those which are going to give the greatest payoff for the least amount of investment in the shortest time. Though this pre-projection of the profile cannot be done to a fine degree of accuracy, attempts to do so to the best of one's ability will be extremely helpful.

As the project develops, a replotting of the profile based upon the newer information at hand can greatly assist in making decisions as to whether to stop the project, slow it down, or speed it up. A careful periodic review of pre-project profiles in comparison with the actual cash flow profile will assist one in sharpening his pre-evaluation methods. It can be easily seen that if one were to develop these profiles for all of the major developments to be undertaken by an organization and add them, he has a projection of the total cash flow for the company. If these profiles have been altered by a probability factor, then this summation can be used to increase or decrease the number of projects depending upon the projected availability of the cash for the company as a whole.

These are a few of the aspects of a cash flow profile chart. There are many others. If no effort along these lines has been made, it is strongly suggested that an attempt be initiated on some major projects. The mental exercise and the sharpening of research planning which will result from this effort is extremely worthwhile. The revision of the chart as different stages are faced is also recommended.

Our final concept, and perhaps the most important concept of all, is based on evaluation through planning (Figure 2). A company research department which is just put out by itself and left alone will, in all likelihood, produce some very useful things, but there may be a wide divergence between these things and what the company really desires. Because of this, it is essential that the research department be guided by a well-defined group of corporate objectives. These objectives can only be defined by

PLANNING & EVALUATION

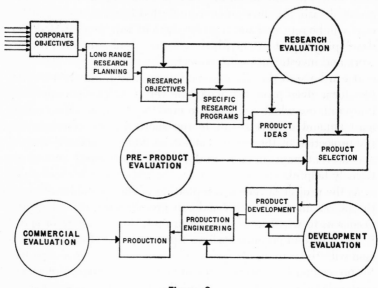

Figure 2

top management, with the assistance of associated departments. The thoughts of finance, planning, marketing, sales, production, engineering, and research can only be combined into a definite group of corporate objectives by top management personnel. After this, the long-range research planning takes place with considerations of the technical and the market aspects. The technical environment includes many such things as competition, scientific disciplines, technical trends in the business, and effects of fundamental research findings. The market environment includes studies of users' needs, population, sociological aspects, economic shifts and competition, and a look at long-range new fields within the company's realm of objectives.

The research planning obviously then leads to and is condensed in certain research objectives. From these research objectives, the technical people must develop specific research programs which are chosen on the basis of existing and future technical situations, internal invention, competition problems, production problems, etc. As the research programs progress, product ideas become evident. Such product ideas must be scanned for feasibility — both technical and marketing. These feasibility studies include probable cost for development and probable returns. In other words, a product decision is made; there follows product development, production engineering, and finally, production and profits.

Now, how do we stand as to evaluation in this cycle? Research evaluation should be possible on the objectives, the specific programs, the ideas, and should also contribute to product selection. Pre-product evaluation applies to product selection. The evaluation of the development phases applies to product development and production engineering. Finally, we have commercial evaluation which always must be in dollars. The degree of success or the degree of safe feeling which can be obtained in each of these steps by evaluation increases as we go down the ladder. It may be possible to attain only a meager evaluation on research objectives or specific research programs. Much more complete evaluation is available on later stages; perhaps 90% or more can be made on the development phases.

The over-all evaluation of the effectiveness of the technical effort can then be made by developing a figure representing the efficiency with which the research objectives are met. Portioning the profits generated by the entire company team, which is a precarious occupation, is then not necessary.

*   *   *   *   *

It is evident that we have a long way to go in the development of methods of evaluation of research and development. We are in a position where certain dollar evaluation can be made on such things as products, processes, and raw materials. Any change of any one of these might cause a corresponding change in another and produce a situation which can be evaluated rather easily. We must recognize certain contributions of research and development without any effort being made to put dollars on them. The views of the company from the outside, from the inside, and from the technical aspect are all important. This problem is like attempting to evaluate certain psychological aspects of the human being in monetary value.

Where do we go? There obviously will be many improvements made in specific dollar evaluation systems for those items which we now can estimate. Likewise, we must recognize that there is no one universal scheme which is usable in all cases. We believe that research is enough a part of big business that continuing efforts will be made and progress will be definite in this field.

We want to caution, however, that complete preoccupation with assessing the value of the technical effort in terms of the profit dollars generated by the whole company can be misleading and perhaps dangerous. It can end up as just another exercise in numbers. Let us not take the inverted and restricted view of the man who said "without numbers there is no science." Our numbering and symbolic system was developed by man to express neatly his concepts of the universe about him. The system has been changed and altered many times in the past. It will be altered in the future as man's mind grasps the meaning of things now beyond him. We believe that the evaluation, and thus improvement in the efficiency of technical efforts, has aspects not yet conceived. If we attempt to evaluate these efforts in terms of their more abstract relation to the total team effort, rather than in a percentage of dollar profits, a really effective method of evaluation and marked improvements in the technical effort will be generated.

Q. (Raymond) You've mentioned the painful analysis of research proposals in which you came up with a need for ten times the capital available or something like that. That would seem to be right because some of the projects *will* fail.

A. That is why probabilities are written into the evaluation. You would be about right in my opinion with no adjusting for probabilities.

Q. . . . Techniques and criteria which can be projected are desirable and certainly no one would argue about their value. But, who is going to apply these criteria? Depending on who applies the criteria, you get quite different results. Do you have your research group try to judge which of these criteria management is going to follow? Research people and operating people would stress different criteria, particularly in group judgments. I'm wondering just how you apply these criteria regarding people.

A. I'd like to stress one thing. As far as I know, most of us look at these things only as comparing one project against another, or one period against another period. Thus, if you use the same technique and generally the same people (who will, of course, improve in their abilities), it works. As Dr. Ansoff said, you know these numbers aren't right; but if you're applying the same judgment to ten projects and one of them gives you a much better number than all the rest, relatively it's a good project. It doesn't say that your number in itself is very meaningful.

Q. You and I were here last fall at the IRI conference at the Harvard Business School where relationships between staff and line were discussed. Didn't we conclude that the line manager is the final judge? Staff should come up with the evaluations only?

A. Companies are trying all types of corporate planning. Some use mixed committees, or the accounting department, or the research department itself, or a new department set up for this. I think you've simply got to watch that these are relevant procedures.

Q. One element of the company may recommend one approach as opposed to another element.

A. Well, that's possible. One of the reasons the IRI has shown intensified interest in this evaluation is that the National Association of Accountants had set up a project to develop a technique for evaluating research. And if the accountants are going to develop a method we feel that we should work with them so that the resulting method eliminates as much divergence of thought as possible.

IMPLICATIONS OF TECHNOLOGY FOR MANAGEMENT

BRUCE D. HENDERSON

BRUCE D. HENDERSON

Vice President
Arthur D. Little, Inc.
Cambridge, Massachusetts

Mr. Henderson received a B.S. degree in Engineering from Vanderbilt University in 1937. In 1941 he obtained his M.B.A. degree from Harvard University Graduate School of Business Administration and then joined Westinghouse Electric Corporation. Here he served through a succession of engineering, marketing, purchasing, and management activities, becoming one of the youngest vice presidents in the history of that company. Since 1959 he has been Vice President in charge of Management Services Division of Arthur D. Little, Inc. In this capacity he is responsible for directing many technical audits and other studies related to the management and implementation of technological progress.

Implications of Technology
for Management

I should like to suggest one more way of looking at the implications of technology for thoughtful management. To state it in the bluntest terms: It is unfortunate when the results of research are wasted. It is a real tragedy when you permit your competitors or outsiders to duplicate your inventions and your own discoveries before your organization is able to use them.

Unlikely as it may seem, this happens. My colleagues have seen this happen not once but many times. To avoid embarrassment, let me take an example from the national scene. I have been led to believe, and I think it is believable, that the United States of America was in a position with hardware, know-how, equipment, and facilities to put a satellite into orbit at least a year before the Russians did. We did not and were not allowed to until the Russians did. Enough of that particular incident except as just one more piece of evidence. When such things happen, you may blame it on personalities, personality clashes, poor management, wrong policies, or on any of many different things, but the result is always the same — too little, too late, or the wrong decision.

Why do these things happen? I suggest that they happen because we are out of phase with our times, late in reacting to events. The most significant fact of our times, overshadowing all else, is the tremendous *rate* of change that we are experiencing. You are in the midst of it, so you may have trouble seeing it. The population explosion, the destructiveness of weapons, the generation of energy, processes, products, insight, all of these things are changing at a *rate* that we have never experienced before. The causes of this increased pace are easy to see. I am sure that someone has said, and others have repeated, during the session that research expenditures are doubling roughly every five or six years. Perhaps they did not say it this way, however: "More money is being spent on research and development now, in this year of 1961, than was spent in the entire period between signing the Declaration of Independence and the end of World War II.

And it was so last year, and it was so the year before." If we have an R & D pipeline that is six, seven, or eight years long, you had better get away from the end of it because a lot of new products, ideas, and techniques are going to start coming out!

We can in a general fashion state what we are faced with. First, you have now a longer feedback loop. Another way of saying it is that more will have happened during the time you require to react. A second fact of life is that the risks are going up. The third one is that, because all your reference points are changing, you are dealing with greater complexity. I do not know how to elaborate such abstract concepts effectively in a short discussion, so let me try to develop a few quick analogies, because I think they will illuminate what I am trying to say.

Take a chess player and introduce this kind of rapid change. Instead of looking at Black's move first, White must make his decision two or three moves before seeing Black's next move. Now, for more complexity, change to three-dimensional chess instead of two-dimensional. Then go from best three-out-of-five to sudden death — lose once and you are out. I think you see what White faces: his reaction time has to go up, his complexity goes up, the risks go up.

* * * * *

You are driving an automobile at night. Now get out of your sports car, get in this truck-trailer, and go twice as fast. Oh, by the way, I am going to cut your headlights down so you cannot see as far ahead. More at stake, less time to react, less time to adjust, more complexity.

* * * * *

This one is easier to translate into the business situation. Move out of this sports airplane and get into a jet. Many of you know the characteristics of a jet in terms of fuel consumption, navigational problems. You pass over radio reporting points so fast that frequently before you finish your regular transmissions you are over the next one. Do not make a mistake in your fuel calculations, you have no alternatives, particularly if you are down low.

How do jet pilots deal with the complexity, the reduction in reaction time, and the greater risk? One thing is fairly certain, they go through far more precise programming. They take a great deal more into account, they look much further into their expected landing environment and what the forecasted weather conditions will be before they take off. Secondly, they rely very much more heavily on the most sophisticated and most precise aids that they can get. No more of this business of flying by the seat of the pants and keeping track of the railroad going through the fog. They must rely on complex and expensive navigational devices as aids. And thirdly, jet pilots impose a very rigid self-discipline on themselves to make sure that they do adhere to these plans because there is no longer the alternative of just feeling your way through it.

I am not trying to reflect on the value of experience or intuitive judgment in management. These things will always be needed. But it is very clear that we are facing a period in which reliance on these to the exclusion of other ways of managing will leave us in serious trouble. This is not the time or the place to try to make a complete inventory of the kinds of tools and techniques suitable for meeting the problems of the new environment. I should, however, like to mention a few of them.

We have borrowed from scientists the use of simulation. One extreme is Dr. Ansoff's mathematical equation, a mathematical simulation of a condition which you implicitly said was too complex to deal with intuitively. I am grateful that he put it up because it at least takes away the accusation of trying to apply precise measurements to things that cannot be precise. When situations get too complex to deal with intuitively, there is no other way of dealing with them in a meaningful fashion. This technique has been applied in a great many fields, and I do not need to tell you what has been done in such areas as inventory control and others where apparently simple judgments have proven to be quite inadequate when put to the test. And great improvements have been possible in areas where reasonably satisfactory results were being achieved before. But one, which I am sure is of interest to you and is at the moment attracting limited attention, is called critical path scheduling — another form of mathematical model-making, mathematical simulation which shows a great deal of promise for reducing the length of time between the laboratory and operations.

Let's talk about one which is not so much a technique as it is a way of looking at the problem: Long-range planning. These words have been used and re-used to the point where they are meaningless in some contexts. But let me describe a characteristic of long-range planning which must be viewed differently from the techniques we have used in the past. You have to combine two things, a predictive task and an evaluative past. You have to combine separately and independently a forecast of the environment in which you will be operating with an evaluation of your capabilities and resources and the relative resources of those who are going to be competing with you in that environment. Like the jet pilot, you have to widen out greatly the scope of the things that you must carefully, specifically, and rather precisely attempt to evaluate. We all know that, but very few companies are organized in such a fashion that this is done on a methodical basis outside of the functions who are interested parties. And if there is anything that the consulting business tells you and tells you repeatedly, it is that the Achilles heel, the chink in the armor of most companies, is the interstice between their major functions. No one except the chief executive is in a position to be disinterested in relationships between functions, yet he is apt to turn this planning over, if he does it at all, to an "assistant to," and he is more concerned with operations, or tends to be, than he is in a long-range picture. So, long-range planning just does not get done in a great many companies.

In the third example, too, we must use names that are loaded, and I ask you to think afresh about "the behavioral sciences." Psychology is a word that has been in everyone's vocabulary since he went to school, but remember that the behavioral sciences are not what they were when you were a student. And remember that as much progress has been made in acquiring insight into these areas as has been made in some of the physical sciences. We have learned a tremendous amount about the behavior of man as an individual, about the behavior of men in groups, about organization relationships, about the characteristics of the environment that are required to produce change. These things are being transferred over into the business community, and they are being applied as tools of management. The technical audits which were mentioned by Jim are a very specific example. Most of our experience has led us to believe that the real problem is research, not what we have been talking about so much but how you get someone to use it. If they do not use it, they do not value it; and, if they do not value it, they will not support it.

Management information systems is my last example of new techniques. Computers are old hat. Everybody know all about computers. Everybody knows how fast they are and how much they can do, particularly that they can turn out a report every month this high, stacked, properly folded, and that it only takes you six weeks to read it. You now say, "I want a condensed report." And you get it! But when you condense that report, you are exercising discrimination, you are determining relative importance, you are determining interplay between parts of the organization, and you have taken over many of the functions of the organization itself. Now, how do you relate your computer to your organization? Because now you have a situation where the machine and the organization are interlaced in a fashion which is incompatible with conventional organization concepts. This is happening and happening very rapidly.

I do not mean to go into any of these new management tools; I do not mean to discuss any of them. I merely mean to mention them as kinds of tools like omni, DME, radar, and Doppler drift indicators that are used on the jet. You must use them now. You cannot put them aside, saying, "I like to fly by the seat of my pants because that is the way I know how."

There is an old military adage, and I am not a military man so I may be misquoting it, that says that the effectiveness of a military organization is limited by three factors: communication, mobility, and firepower. It does not do any good to have the firepower unless you have the mobility to get it where you need it; it does not do any good to be able to get it where you need it unless you have the communication to know where you need it. If any one of these three lags very far behind the other two, this is a constraint on effectiveness. Let me draw you a parallel. I consider technology as the businessman's firepower, and, for the first time in human history, it looks as though it is going to outstrip the other two. That may make little difference because it may develop faster than you can digest it. Look upon management information as communications, and look, for mobility, to the behavioral sciences. I merely ask you to consider whether perhaps you should be giving as much thought to these other two as you are to the firepower.

I hope you will not mind another military parallel. After all man has had more experience with large-scale organization in military activity than he has in any other fashion. And military organizations by their very nature are faced with the problem of dealing with rapid change at some time in the future. I think this is probably the reason that military general staff work has been far more formalized and far more effective than it has in business. Many people attribute the success of the German army in World War I to the general staff, and I have heard people say that if that intuitive manager, Hitler, had left the general staff alone, World War II might have come out a little bit differently in some ways. I think we might well take a look at this generalized staff to see if there is any value in it for business.

I commend to you three of its characteristics as appropriate in a business environment. One is that it must be nonfunctional; it must not be tied to the interest of one particular segment of the business no matter how important. The reason for this is that characteristically any one segment of the business has a strong tendency to assume that the others are hard to change, hard to move, and therefore must be considered permanent. Therefore, all that you can change is that which is in the purview of your own particular function. So the general staff has to get outside of all the functions. The second thing, and this is implicit in all I said, it must deal with the whole picture. And third, it must stay away from operations and deal with the future; otherwise it gets into the question of evaluation not of resources, not of capability, but of personalities and operational problems, and the two are different fields.

Now — what have we said here? You came to this meeting because you are part of the leading edge of this revolution. The change is hitting you, not only in your environment, but in your daily work. What can you do about it? I can suggest some things that seem to be worth thinking about. One is that we are going to need considerably greater skill in this generalized staff function. It seems rather clear that we must formalize our planning activities to make certain that they are fully and completely done. We must expand them so that we look at many environmental factors beyond the narrow ones that we have in the past (i.e., what our competitors are likely to do before we do it). I think we can make one other fairly safe conclusion: that people are not going to accept change as fast as technology will demand it. Our insights might change, but not people. Therefore, we are quite likely to outrun our ability to adapt the new technology to the same old human beings. Unless, of course, we can provide the same thoughtful care and attention to this that we have to our physical problems.

I would like to leave you with two thoughts: There is no precedent for the situation you are in. Your lifetime has encompassed more change than all of humanity before you. Apparently this is only the beginning. You should think very carefully about all the implications. And the other thought: "Isn't it an unfortunate thing when the results of research are wasted and isn't it a tragedy when you permit your competitors or outsiders to duplicate your inventions and your own discoveries before your organization is able to use them?"

Q. Mr. Henderson, do you think the development of management information systems has any chance of catching up with the increasing pressure of assimilating stuff which we generate? At the rate we're going now, information generation is a thousand miles ahead of assimilation.

A. That is true. Good management information systems can provide for more information than the recipient can digest or assimilate. That is why such systems must screen certain material and interpret other material. This in itself is a decision-making process. That is why management information systems are truly a part of the organization structure — not just a calculation. Management information systems are already ahead of our organization arrangements.

Q. Well, I don't think we can stop the changes because there are a vast number of people in industry who aren't going to do anything, and who are not going too fast.

A. I agree that some, perhaps many, will not be able to stand the pace and will fall by the wayside.

SUMMARY

JAMES R. BRIGHT

We have, by inference, shown that today's rate of technological change means that there is little security in the status quo. Security in any present business environment is decreasing; and probably it is decreasing at different rates for various industries and companies. Opportunities for new businesses are arising at a significant rate. If this notion is correct, it leads me to suggest that each individual might take home four questions:

1. Is my firm structured so that it is capable of receiving, appraising, and implementing new technological ideas?
2. Do we have a group or person with the responsibility for a continuous reappraisal of our firm's future environment, and of the prospects for technological changes, and of other changes that might affect our present business?
3. Do we truly encourage technological innovation, recognizing that some failures surely will be encountered — that the more we innovate, that the "further out" we are — the higher the percentage of failure may be? And that, on the other hand, the rewards may be greater?
4. Are our managers and we ourselves truly receptive to new ideas?

It seemed to me that our speakers did a fine job of putting a much more structured framework around these four questions as focused on technological change. If you were satisfied with your answers to these questions, then, of course, you wouldn't have come. But all of you have indicated to the speakers by your interest that you are not satisfied with many of the answers you are presently getting.

I can close only after expressing my deepest personal thanks to a splendid set of contributors. One participant after another has privately said to me that it has been a very worthwhile affair. On behalf of the Harvard Business School, may I say that your enthusiasm has been the School's reward. Thank you, gentlemen. The conference is over.